CORROSION in ACTION

General Supervision by . . . *F. L. LaQue*
Technical Direction by . . . *T. P. May*
Consultant . . . *H. H. Uhlig*

THE INTERNATIONAL NICKEL COMPANY, INC.

67 Wall Street, New York 5, N. Y.

CONTENTS

☆ ☆ ☆ ☆ ☆ ☆ ☆ ☆ ☆ ☆ ☆ ☆

☆ ☆ ☆ ☆ ☆ ☆ ☆ ☆ ☆ ☆ ☆ ☆

The text of this book is essentially the narrative of the motion picture "Corrosion in Action". In its present form this narrative is supplemented by appropriate references to literature which will provide more detailed information on particular points. In addition, there is a description of the experiments shown in the film so that these can be undertaken by any students who may have an opportunity to study the subject in the laboratory.

The film itself was produced by Inco as an aid to the understanding of some of the electrochemical processes that result in corrosion. It was felt that a knowledge of these principles would improve the basis for action in avoiding corrosion by choosing the proper materials and using them to best advantage. As stated in the final paragraph, the goal is to have the right metal used in the right way in the right place. It is hoped that making the substance of the film available for ready reference in this form will prove to be a useful supplement to the motion picture itself in achieving this objective.

The Nature of Corrosion
Anode and Cathode Processes

In nature the forces that cause corrosion are as constantly in action as the sea. Everyone has seen corrosion turn useful structures into crumbling skeletons, productive machines into frozen hulks, automobiles into piles of junk. It costs more than 6 billion dollars in a year.[1] It dissipates our resources and the fruits of our labor. It interrupts production. It causes accidents.

Different metals are affected to different degrees and corrosive attack takes many different forms. Attack may be by general tarnishing or rusting with occasional perforations in especially affected areas[2] (1). Corrosion may develop preferentially near the junction of two different metals[3] (2). The metal may suffer highly localized attack by pitting[4] (3). The strength of a metal may be destroyed by cracking induced by corrosion[5] (4). We are all too familiar with corrosion in action in these ways. Corrosion may also be confined to crevices, under gaskets or washers, or in sockets[6] (5). It may have the effect of removing one of the constituents of an alloy so as to leave a weak residue[7] (6).

The study of corrosion considers reactions between a metal and its environment (7). It also concerns the suppression of corrosion by changing the characteristics of metals and their environments. The great progress in the battle against corrosion has been based on a better understanding of the natural forces concerned and on the development of the scientific principles upon which effective control of corrosion must be based.

It is possible to explain how this action occurs and what can be done to reduce it by illustrating some of these principles. From the start, educational institutions and research laboratories have contributed greatly to the scientific basis of corrosion. Some of the most important principles go back to early investigators. Michael Faraday studied alloying of iron[8] and contributed much

(1) Perforation of steel due to corrosion that is apparent in the form of rust.

(2) Galvanic corrosion of magnesium where it is in close contact with a steel core around which the magnesium was cast.

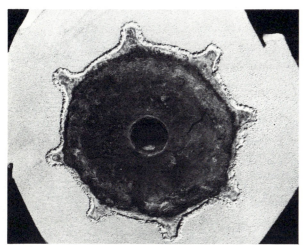

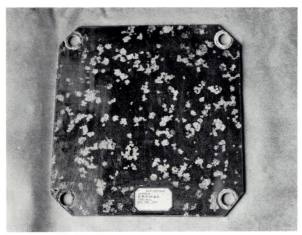

(3) Pitting on a metal surface resulting from localized corrosion under marine organisms that became attached to the surface while immersed in sea water.

(4) Cracking induced in the metal as a result of a combination of corrosion and high tensile stresses.

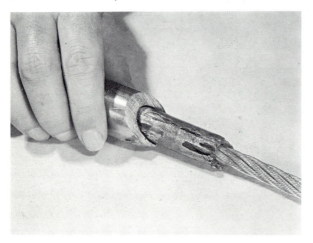

(5) Severe corrosion that occurred in crevice of a mooring pennant.

(6) Graphite residue remaining as a result of corrosion of cast iron elbow.

to the fundamental knowledge of electrochemistry.[9] Sir Humphrey Davy[10] worked out the essential details of galvanic corrosion and cathodic protection back in 1824 when he initiated the use of zinc to control corrosion of ships' hulls (8). Richard Adie[11] in 1847 demonstrated the generation of current and corrosion caused by differences in oxygen at the surface of iron in different locations in a flowing stream.

With the scientific background provided by these many early students, Dr. Willis Rodney Whitney[12] worked out and expressed in its most useful form one of the principles which constitute the basic structure for modern methods of corrosion control. In 1903 when Dr. Whitney was divid-

ing his time between the research laboratory that he had founded at the General Electric Company and his duties as a Professor at the Massachusetts Institute of Technology, he investigated the corrosion of some steel pipes in water. By subjecting specimens of iron to the corrosive action of water under conditions simulating those encountered in service, he sought to discover under what conditions iron will corrode and what factors influence the rate of attack.

From his experiments Dr. Whitney concluded, "Practically the only factor which limits the life of iron is oxidation, under which name are included all the chemical processes whereby the iron is corroded, eaten away, or rusted. In under-

(7) Various materials undergoing atmospheric exposure corrosion tests in Inco Station at Kure Beach, North Carolina.

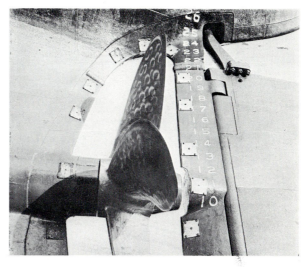

(8) Zinc anodes attached to the stern frame of an ocean-going vessel.

(9) Corrosion products of iron in the form of iron rust on a sample that had been exposed to the atmosphere.

(10) Natural iron ore.

going this change, the iron always passes through or into a state of solution, and as we have no evidence of iron going into aqueous solution except in the form of ions, we have really to consider the effects of conditions upon the potential difference between iron and its surroundings. The whole subject of corrosion of iron is, therefore, an electrochemical one, and the rate of corrosion is simply a function of electromotive force and resistance of circuit." Dr. Whitney thus concluded that corrosion is electrochemical in nature like the action taking place in a dry cell.

The application of the electrochemical principles developed by these investigators provides the means for modern methods of corrosion control. The basic cause of corrosion is the instability of metals in their refined forms. Because of this free energy relationship, the metals tend to revert to their natural states through the processes of corrosion. In the case of iron the action of rain forms rust. When you analyze rust, you find it is iron oxide (9). When you analyze natural iron ore, you find it too is iron oxide (10). In rusting, iron has reverted to its original native state.

To begin with, the basic nature of corrosion is

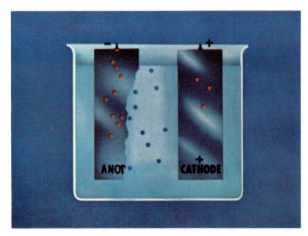

(11) Flow of electricity between anode and cathode in the corrosion of a metal.

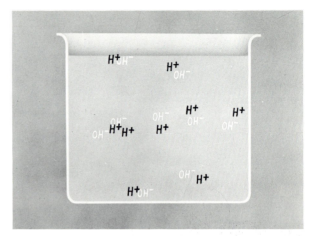

(12) Hydrogen and hydroxyl ions from the ionization of ordinary water.

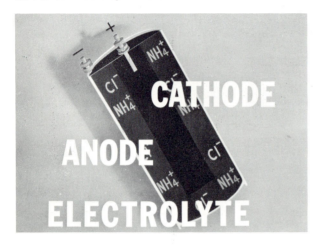

(13) Cut-away showing the graphite cathode, zinc anode and ions from ammonium chloride in an ordinary dry cell.

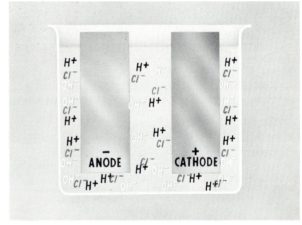

(14) Illustration of the anode, cathode and ions in a corrosive solution.

almost always the same—a flow of electricity between certain areas of a metal surface through a solution capable of conducting an electric current (11). This electrochemical action causes destructive alteration or eating away of a metal at areas which are called anodes where the electric current leaves the metal and enters the solution. It is the critical step in the series of events we associate with corrosion.

We have the presence of an electrolyte as one of the first requirements of corrosion. An electrolyte, as we know, is any liquid that contains ions. Ions, you remember, are electrically charged atoms, or groups of atoms, in solution. Pure water, for example, contains positively charged hydrogen

ions and negatively charged hydroxyl ions in equal concentration (12). A single drop of water may contain about 3 million-million hydrogen ions and an equal number of hydroxyl ions. So our corrosive environment may be any form of moisture ranging from plain water to the strongest acid, or the strongest alkali. It may be just moisture condensed from the air or it may be salt water. But, in any environment regardless of its nature, the basic mechanism of corrosion is in principle the same as the electrochemical action in an electric dry cell, such as we have all seen (13). There is always an electrolyte that contains many ions, and we must have two electrodes, an anode and a cathode, where current enters the metal from the electrolyte. These electrodes may consist of two different kinds of metal (14), or they may be different areas on the same piece of metal. In either case, there must be a potential difference between the two electrodes, or areas, so that electricity will flow between them. A wire or metallic path is necessary to complete the circuit for the flow of electrons (15), which are negatively charged particles moving in the wire from the negative to the positive. The popular concept of current flow as used in this discussion visualizes imaginary positive charges moving in the opposite direction. This electron path may be provided by any kind of metallic bridge, or merely by the fact that the two metals are in contact with each other.

Let us consider what takes place at the anode when corrosion occurs. Positively charged atoms of metal detach themselves from the solid surface and enter into solution as ions while the corresponding negative charges, in the form of electrons, are left behind in the metal (16). The detached positive ions bear one or more positive charges. In the corrosion of iron, each iron atom releases two electrons and becomes an iron ion carrying two positive charges. The released electrons travel through the metal to the cathode area.

What has been taking place at the cathode all this time? The electrons reaching the surface of the cathode through the metal meet and neutralize some positively charged hydrogen ions which have arrived at the same surface through the electrolyte (17). In losing their charge, the positive

(15) Illustration of wire as a metallic path necessary to complete the circuit for the flow of electrons in a corrosion cell.

ions become neutral atoms again, and may combine to form hydrogen gas. The release of hydrogen ions results in the accumulation of a relatively high concentration of OH^- ions which are left behind to increase the alkalinity at the cathode or to make the solution less acid.

Briefly then, for corrosion to occur, there must

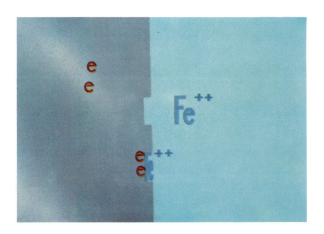

(16) Formation of ferrous ions in the corrosion of iron.

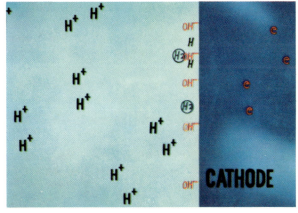

(17) Reduction of hydrogen ions at cathode to form hydrogen atoms and subsequently hydrogen molecules (gas). Hydroxyl ions are also formed.

(18) Illustration of the overall process as occurring at the anode and cathode areas during corrosion in a solution containing ions.

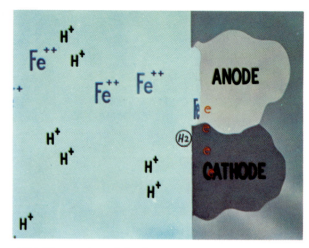

(19) Illustration of the formation of ions at the anode and hydrogen at the cathode in local cell action.

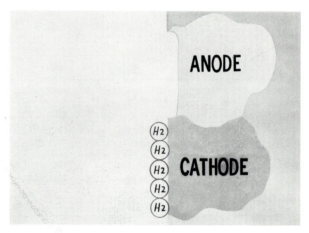

(20) Polarization of the local cathode by a film of hydrogen.

be a release of electrons at the anode, and a formation of metal ions through oxidation and disintegration of the metal. At the cathode, there must be a simultaneous acceptance of the electrons such as by neutralization of positive ions or formation of negative ions (18). Action at the anode cannot go on alone, nor can action at the cathode. As first established by Michael Faraday, the two reactions go on at the same time at equivalent rates. But corrosion, the disintegration itself, occurs almost always at areas that act as anodes.

If we place a piece of ordinary iron in a solution of hydrochloric acid, we obtain a vigorous formation of hydrogen bubbles. Under such conditions, the metal corrodes very quickly. The usual dissolution of the metal is occurring only at the anodes, with hydrogen bubbles forming only at the cathodes even though it may appear that they are being released all over the surface rather than at well-defined cathodic areas. The anodic and cathodic areas may shift from time to time. This permits substantially uniform corrosion to occur.

If we could see this action through a powerful microscope, we would see many tiny anode and cathode areas on the surface of the metal. These areas are often so small as to be invisible, and so numerous as to be almost inseparable. There are many causes for this: such as inclusions in the metal, lack of homogeneity, surface imperfections, orientation of grains, localized stresses and variations in environment.[13] If we could see just one anode and one cathode in a giant view (19), we would see electrons released by the formation of ferrous ions flowing through the metal from the anode to the cathode, where they meet the hydrogen ions in solution which act as electron acceptors at the cathode surface, one electron being accepted in the discharge of one hydrogen ion. The hydrogen then appears as hydrogen gas coating the metal surface. So as this process continues, oxidation and corrosion of iron occurs at the anodes, and plating out of hydrogen occurs at the cathodes. This formation of hydrogen molecules and the evolution of hydrogen gas are the principal reactions in corrosion by acids, as in this example. But, in neutral electrolytes, such as a

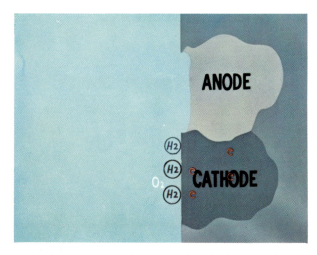

(21) *Removal of hydrogen or depolarization of cathode by oxygen in the solution.*

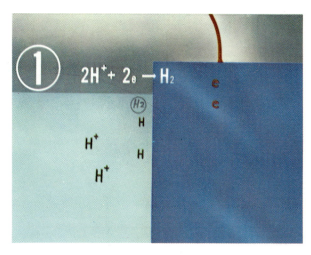

(22) *Cathodic reaction: Reduction of hydrogen ions to hydrogen gas.*

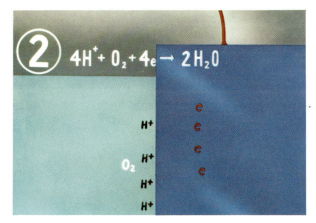

(23) *Cathodic reaction: Reduction of oxygen to form water.*

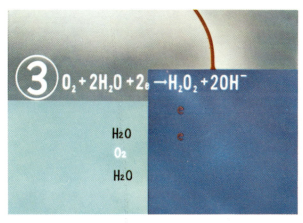

(24) *Cathodic reaction: Reduction of oxygen to form hydrogen peroxide and hydroxyl ions.*

sodium chloride solution, the evolution of hydrogen gas is very slow, and the accumulation of a layer of hydrogen on the metal slows down the reaction by a process we call cathodic polarization (20).

However, reactions involving oxygen dissolved in the electrolyte can occur to complete the cathodic reaction (21). Oxygen can react with the accumulated hydrogen to form water, and by removing it this way, permit corrosion to proceed. In doing this, oxygen acts as a cathodic depolarizer. Therefore, the cathodic reactions can involve either hydrogen evolution or some reaction with oxygen. Reaction 1 represents the liberation of hydrogen (22). Reaction 2 is the oxidation of

hydrogen by dissolved oxygen to form water (23). Other possible reactions are the reduction of oxygen in water to form hydrogen peroxide and hydroxyl ions as in equation 3 (24), or completely to hydroxyl ions as in equation 4[14] (25).

The products of the anode and cathode processes frequently meet and enter into further reactions that yield many of our common visible corrosion products. For example, with iron in water the hydroxyl ions from the cathodic reaction in their migration through the electrolyte towards the anode encounter ferrous ions moving in the opposite direction. These ions combine to form ferrous hydroxide (26). This soon becomes oxidized by oxygen in solution to form ferric hydroxide which precipitates as a form of iron rust with which we are all too familiar (27). Depending on the alkalinity, oxygen content and agitation of the solution, this rust may form either away from the iron surface or right next to it where it can exert more of an influence on the further progress of corrosion.

The action of oxygen in furthering corrosion is easily demonstrated by placing iron turnings in two flasks filled with water (28). Oxygen is allowed to bubble through the water in one flask to supply it with oxygen. The water in the second flask is saturated with nitrogen to keep oxygen out of solution. After the gases bubble for several hours, one finds that the iron in the oxygen-free solution is as bright as ever, but the iron in the water saturated with oxygen has already begun to rust. So the oxygen content of any solution ranks high on the list of factors influencing corrosion. For this reason, oxygen is removed from boiler waters to reduce corrosion of the boiler. Deaeration of industrial waters is being increasingly applied as a measure of corrosion control.[15]

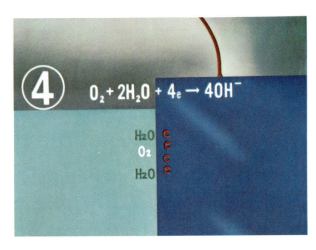

(25) *Cathodic reaction: Reduction of oxygen to form hydroxyl ions.*

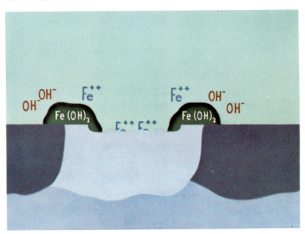

(26) *Formation of ferrous hydroxide in the rusting of iron.*

(28)*Reduction of corrosion of iron in water by the removal of oxygen illustrated by bubbling oxygen through one solution and nitrogen through a second one.*

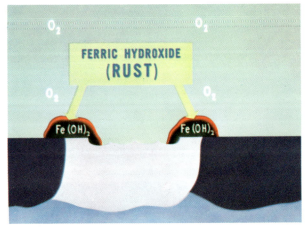

(27) *Conversion of ferrous hydroxide into ferric hydroxide by the action of oxygen.*

Origin and Characteristics of Corrosion Currents

In the list of causes of corrosion are differences in the electrical potential of dissimilar metals coupled together and immersed in an electrolyte. The resulting corrosion is known as galvanic action. Differences in potential from point to point on a single metal surface cause corrosion known as local action. This type may be due to such causes as impurities on the surface or differences in surface structure or to differences in the environment next to the metal. When we understand the source of corrosion currents, we can change metals and their environments so that the sources of such currents are minimized, if not eliminated. Some of these conditions can be examined in much more detail. For example, when considering galvanic corrosion, it is essential to know which metal in the couple will suffer accelerated corrosion. This is indicated in a rough way by the positions of metals in the Standard Electromotive Series, below.

The gas hydrogen is used as an arbitrary reference element. As we move up the list from hydrogen, one after another the metals become increasingly reactive. Similarly, as we go down from hydrogen, the metals become increasingly inert. For example, if we put a piece of potassium in water, we get a violent reaction. Whereas we can place a piece of platinum in strong nitric acid with no evidence of attack. These are extremes that illustrate a general rule. The electromotive series also shows which metals can displace other metals in solution and suffer corrosion in the process. Any metal may displace one below it in this series. For example, iron can displace copper from

ELECTROMOTIVE FORCE SERIES

Electrode Reaction	Standard Electrode Potential, E° (Volts), 25°C	Electrode Reaction	Standard Electrode Potential, E° (Volts), 25° C
$K = K^+ + e^-$	−2.922	$Ni = Ni^{++} + 2e^-$	−0.250
$Ca = Ca^{++} + 2e^-$	−2.87	$Sn = Sn^{++} + 2e^-$	−0.136
$Na = Na^+ + e^-$	−2.712	$Pb = Pb^{++} + 2e^-$	−0.126
$Mg = Mg^{++} + 2e^-$	−2.34	$H2 = 2H^+ + 2e^-$	0.000
$Be = Be^{++} + 2e^-$	−1.70	$Cu = Cu^{++} + 2e^-$	0.345
$Al = Al^{+++} + 3e^-$	−1.67	$Cu = Cu^+ + e^-$	0.522
$Mn = Mn^{++} + 2e^-$	−1.05	$2Hg = Hg2^{++} + 2e^-$	0.799
$Zn = Zn^{++} + 2e^-$	−0.762	$Ag = Ag^+ + e^-$	0.800
$Cr = Cr^{+++} + 3e^-$	−0.71	$Pd = Pd^{++} + 2e^-$	0.83
$Ga = Ga^{+++} + 3e^-$	−0.52	$Hg = Hg^{++} + 2e^-$	0.854
$Fe = Fe^{++} + 2e^-$	−0.440	$Pt = Pt^{++} + 2e^-$	ca 1.2
$Cd = Cd^{++} + 2e^-$	−0.402	$Au = Au^{+++} + 3e^-$	1.42
$In = In^{+++} + 3e^-$	−0.340	$Au = Au^+ + e^-$	1.68
$Tl = Tl^+ + e^-$	−0.336		
$Co = Co^{++} + 2e^-$	−0.277		

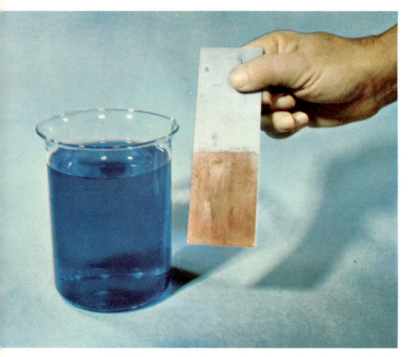

(29) *Copper film formed on iron when iron displaces copper from copper sulfate solution.*

solution with the copper ions acting as the acceptors for electrons in the corrosion of the iron (29). The displaced copper appears as a coating on the corroded iron surface. Similarly, hydrogen ions can act as electron acceptors for any metal above hydrogen in the electromotive series as in the case of zinc in hydrochloric acid (30). Metals below hydrogen in the series do not readily displace hydrogen from solution, and, therefore, are more resistant to corrosion, as in the case of copper dipped into the same hydrochloric acid as the zinc. On the other hand, copper can displace silver from solution with the silver ions here acting as the electron acceptors in the corrosion of copper (31).

This electromotive series holds only for metals in particular concentrations of their own salts. In other electrolytes, the performance may be different. In studying galvanic action[3], we use instead of the electromotive series a somewhat similar galvanic series based on experience with combinations of metals in a great variety of environments. The table shown on page 15 provides such a series for a number of metals and alloys in sea water moving at high velocity.

(30) *Displacement of hydrogen from hydrochloric acid by zinc.*

(31) *Film of silver on copper formed when copper displaced silver from silver nitrate solution.*

GALVANIC SERIES OF METALS AND ALLOYS IN SEA WATER

Magnesium
Zinc
Alclad 3S
Aluminum 3S
Aluminum 61S
Aluminum 63S
Aluminum 52
Low Steel
Alloy Steel
Cast Iron
Type 410 (Active)
Type 430 (Active)
Type 304 (Active)
Type 316 (Active)
Ni-Resist* corrosion-resisting, nickel
    cast iron
Muntz Metal
Yellow Brass
Admiralty Brass
Aluminum Brass
Red Brass
Copper
Aluminum Bronze
Composition G Bronze
90/10 Copper-Nickel
70/30 Copper-Nickel—Low Iron
70/30 Copper-Nickel—High Iron
Nickel
Inconel* nickel-chromium alloy
Silver
Type 410 (Passive)
Type 430 (Passive)
Type 304 (Passive)
Type 316 (Passive)
Monel* nickel-copper alloy
Hastelloy** Alloy C
Titanium

In any couple, the metal near the top of this series will be the anode and suffer accelerated corrosion in a galvanic couple, while the one nearer the bottom will be the cathode and receive some galvanic protection. The specimen of magnesium cast around a steel core illustrates galvanic action (32). Magnesium at the top of the scale is the

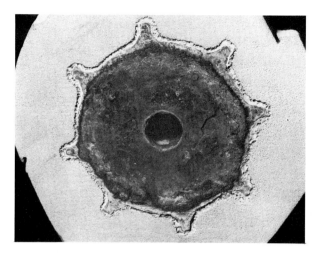

(32) Galvanic corrosion of magnesium where it is in close contact with a steel core around which the magnesium was cast.

more active metal and has suffered galvanic corrosion. Except for the extremes, any given metal may be an anode or a cathode depending on the other metal with which it is coupled and their galvanic relationship in the environment encountered.

Now the question is what determines the speed at which galvanic corrosion will proceed. One factor is the degree of difference in electric potential between the two metals. A metal coupled with another close to it in this list will usually corrode more slowly than when coupled with one further below it. To illustrate, zinc coupled with aluminum in sodium chloride solution will generate a potential of about 300 millivolts (33); whereas with zinc and copper in the same solution, the potential is over 700 millivolts (34). The greater the potential, the greater will be the driving force behind the galvanic corrosion. Furthermore, as the galvanic corrosion reaction proceeds, there is an accumulation of reaction products at the anode and at the cathode. This causes the initial potential or driving force to diminish. The potential of the anode drifts toward that of the cathode, and that of the cathode drifts toward that of the anode (35). This is analogous to the change in the difference in level between a liquid in two vessels when it flows from one to the other (36). This change in potential is called polarization; that at the anode, anodic polarization; and that at the cathode, cathodic polarization.

*INCO Trademark
**Trademark Union Carbide Corporation

(33) Potential of 300 millivolts between zinc and aluminum in sodium chloride solution.

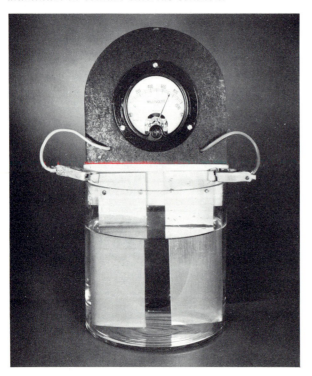

(34) Potential of 700 millivolts between zinc and copper in sodium chloride solution.

In the corrosion reactions with which we are most likely to be concerned, the polarization that occurs at the cathodes exerts more of a controlling influence than the lesser degree of polarization at the anodes.[3n] Consequently, what happens at the cathode has greater practical importance. This can be an accumulation of hydrogen so as in effect to cover cathodic surfaces and thereby restrain corrosion at the anodes until the hydrogen is removed by one or another of the cathodic reactions, such as evolution as gain or union with oxygen to form water.

These cathodic reactions do not proceed with equal facility on all metal surfaces. As a result, some metals polarize more readily than others (37), and it is necessary to know something about

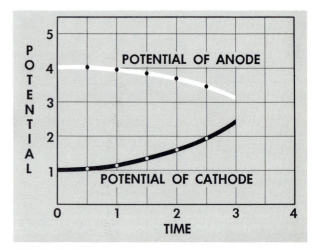

(35) Polarization of anode and cathode vs. time.

(36) Hydraulic analogy of anodic and cathodic polarization.

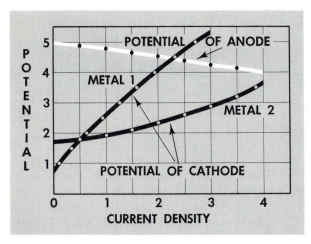

(37) Polarization of metals vs. current density.

polarization characteristics as well as initial potentials before we can predict the extent of galvanic corrosion with any particular couple of metals.

This change in potential we call polarization is a function not just of current but of current density. This can be illustrated by another analogy.

(38) Hydraulic analogy illustrating polarization as a function of current density.

If we pour a given quantity of liquid into a small vessel, it will fill it to a higher level than if we pour the same quantity into a larger vessel (38). Similarly, for the same amount of current, the current density on a small electrode will be greater than on a large electrode. For example, with a large cathode the hydrogen that reaches it will be spread out and will be more accessible for re-

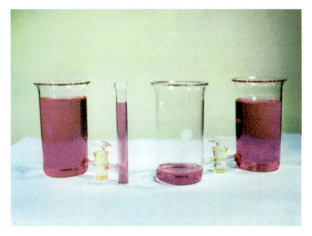

(39) Hydraulic analogy illustrating polarization as a function of current density.

moval by reaction with oxygen. This can be illustrated by still another hydraulic analogy where liquid flows from one vessel into another (39). If the receiving vessel is small, representing high current density, the level in it will rise more quickly and the unit will come to equilibrium faster than if the receiving vessel is large, representing low current density.

A direct example of this effect in galvanic corrosion is provided by an experiment in which pieces of steel of the same size are connected in an aerated salt solution to pieces of copper of different sizes, one small and one large (40). Both couples generate current, but the couple with the large cathode produces the higher current. When the supply of oxygen is cut off and cathodic polarization is allowed to occur, it will be observed that the current drops off faster in the couple with the small cathode than it does with the large cathode, just as the flow of liquid into the small vessel stopped before it did with the larger one. To show again the action of oxygen as a cathodic depolarizer, all we need

(40) *Influence of cathode area on corrosion current illustrated by steel-copper couples in sodium chloride solution. Area of copper cathode in right hand cell about five times area of copper in left hand cell.*

(41) *Influence of area relationship between cathode and anode illustrated by copper-steel couples after immersion in sea water. Above: Copper rivets with small area in steel plates of large area have caused only slight increase in corrosion of steel. Below: Steel rivets with small area in copper plates of large area have caused severe corrosion of steel rivets.*

do is restore the flow of oxygen and watch how the corrosion current increases once more. We can now understand why it is hazardous to couple a large cathode with a small anode.[3m] The increased corrosion where the area of the cathode is relatively large is demonstrated by immersing riveted plates in sea water for several months (41). One of these plates consists of two pieces of steel joined by copper rivets. After immersion in sea water, the copper rivets are still in good condition, and there is no significant acceleration of the corrosion of the steel in their immediate vicinity. The second plate consisting of two pieces of copper joined by steel rivets presents a sharp contrast to the first plate. The steel rivets have been attacked very severely. The metals are the same in each case but the unfavorable area relationship of the large copper cathode and small steel anode was responsible for the severe galvanic corrosion of the steel rivets.

The same type of cell that develops between two different metals may also develop on a single metal surface. Differences in potential from point to point can be created by differences in environment.[6a] For example, the concentration of metal ions in the corroding solution at one point on the metal surface may become greater than at another point (42), with the metal in contact with the solution of greater metal ion concentration be-

coming the cathode and the metal in contact with the lower concentration acting as the anode and being corroded. This will cause electricity to flow between the two points. We can demonstrate these facts with a two compartment glass cell in each side of which we have a copper specimen with a concentrated solution of copper sulfate in one side and a dilute solution in the other side (43). Thus, we can establish two separate environments containing different concentrations of the same metal ion. Using electrical instruments, we observe a 50 millivolt difference in potential and a current flow of nearly 400 microamperes between the two copper electrodes. This demonstration proves that we have one more cause of corrosion currents.

Such differences in metal ion concentration can be set up where a metal is in contact with a

(42) Concentration gradient in a copper sulfate solution.

(43) Copper ion concentration cell. Dilute copper sulfate solution on left separated from concentrated copper sulfate solution on right by porous membrane.

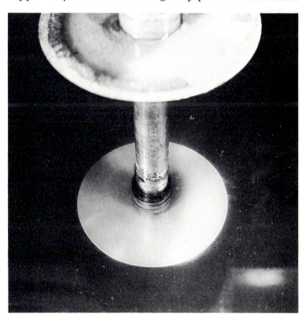

(44) Arrangement for rotating metal disc in sea water.

solution where the relative movement or velocity is greater at one point than another. This situation can be created by spinning a copper alloy disc through salt water (44). The metal nearer the center of the disc moves more slowly than at the periphery. This allows metal ions to accumulate in and under films that develop near the center while they are swept away from the metal near the periphery. This results in severe corrosion in the region of highest velocity where the metal ion concentration is least (45). The effects of these cells can be avoided by proper choice of composition of alloy to suit the velocity conditions to be encountered, as in the case of the Monel nickel-copper alloy disc (46), which was able to hold its protective film right up to the outer edge when it was whirled through the water and thus avoided the development of the destructive metal ion concentration cells.

Oxygen concentration cells can also be set up to cause equally destructive corrosion. Cathodes develop at the areas of high oxygen concentration, and anodes at the areas of low concentration where corrosion occurs (47). The fact that electricity does flow between points where oxygen concentrations differ may be demonstrated with similar pieces of steel in each side of a two compartment cell containing a dilute sodium chloride solution (48). No current flows when they are coupled through a microammeter; but if we bubble nitrogen through one side of the cell to reduce

(45) *Severe corrosion in region of high velocity on an admiralty brass disc after rotation in sea water.*

(46) *Monel nickel-copper alloy disc after rotation in sea water illustrating complete lack of velocity attack due to proper choice of alloy.*

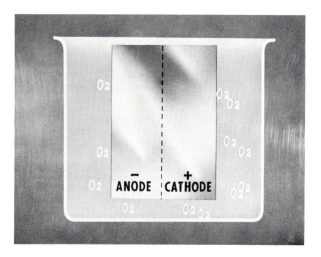

(47) *Illustrating difference in oxygen concentration in a solution covering a single metal surface.*

(48) *Oxygen concentration cell established on steel in sodium chloride solution. Oxygen concentration reduced by nitrogen in left hand compartment and high oxygen concentration achieved with oxygen bubbling through right hand compartment. The two compartments are separated by a porous membrane.*

the oxygen concentration, and oxygen through the other side to increase the oxygen content, we find electricity flowing, proving the existence of a corrosion current. So we know that differences in oxygen concentrations will also set up corrosive conditions.

The existence and location of anodes and cathodes in an oxygen concentration corrosion cell on a steel surface can be demonstrated by the changes in color of certain reagents as well as by the use of electrical instruments as in the preceding experiment. We have shown that the cathode reaction produces an increase in the concentration of hydroxyl ions as a result of removal of hydrogen ions or the reduction of oxygen. Phenolphthalein is a well-known indicator which develops a red color when the concentration of hydroxyl ions is increased (49). Therefore, if phenolphthalein turns red as corrosion proceeds, it will detect the existence of a cathode and reveal where it is.

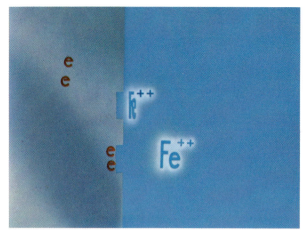

(49) Red color developed at cathode by phenolphthalein indicator in presence of hydroxyl ions.

(50) Blue color developed at iron anode due to interaction between ferrous ions and potassium ferricyanide.

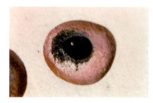

(51) Phenolphthalein and potassium ferricyanide indicators reveal location of cathode at periphery of drop and anode in center of drop due to differential aeration.

Similarly, potassium ferricyanide is a reagent which produces a blue color by reaction with ferrous ions (50) such as are formed at the anodic areas when iron corrodes. The appearance of this blue color, therefore, demonstrates the existence and location of anodes on iron. Using these reagents we can show the development and location of the anode and cathode in a cell established on an iron surface within a drop of a gel containing these indicators (51). Oxygen from the air is more accessible to the periphery of the drop and sets up a cathode there as shown by a pink color. Simultaneously, an anode, shown by the blue color, develops near the center of the drop which is less accessible to oxygen.

Most frequently the conditions that give rise to oxygen concentration cell attack are associated with the presence of a deposit at one point on an otherwise freely exposed surface (52). The metal outside the deposit will be readily accessible to oxygen while that under the deposit will be shielded from it. This will set up a corrosion cell with the formation of metal ions in the anodic region under the deposit. Electrons will flow

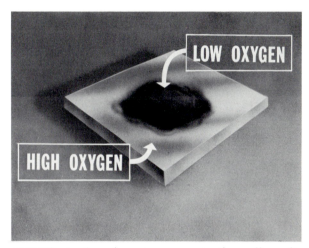

(52) Illustration of oxygen concentration cell resulting from a deposit on a metal surface.

through the metal to the surface outside the deposit, and a cathodic reaction there will result in the reduction of oxygen to form hydroxyl ions. For example, a little pile of sand on part of an otherwise clean surface of brass will lead to accelerated attack under the sand (53). One of the pioneers in pointing out the importance to corrosion theory of these concentration cells was R. J. McKay of The International Nickel Company, Inc. who observed [6a] "My tests in 1921 and 22 indicated that serious corrosion such as just described would occur from electrolytic cells entirely due to differences of concentration in the solution. These cells might be due to dif-

(53) Oxygen concentration cell attack under a pile of sand on brass.

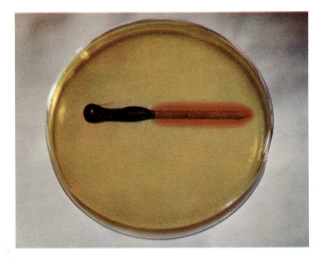

(54) Anode and cathode on partially copper plated iron nail indicated by colors developed with phenolphthalein and potassium ferricyanide indicators.

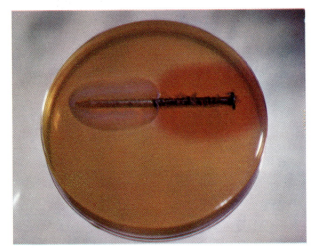

(55) Location of anode and cathode areas on an iron nail partially plated with zinc.

ferent concentrations of dissolved air or metal salts, both of which you have seen, or they might be due to different concentrations of other dissolved gases or acids, or a range of oxidizing and reducing salts, so they might occur frequently and under many diverse circumstances. For instance, any condition which will give a plentiful supply of air to one part of a solution while another part is short of air will cause these cells; but the most striking and important characteristic of the cell is that paradoxically corrosion occurs where the concentration of corroding agent is low. In the case of a uniform metal surface, you can start corrosion on one point merely by partially shielding it from the corroding agent. This was illustrated by the case of sand on brass."

The color changing reagents used previously to demonstrate oxygen concentration cells can be used as well to show the existence and location of anodes and cathodes in other types of corrosion cells such as may be set up between dissimilar metals or from point to point on a single metal surface. For example, upon placing an iron nail with copper plate on the pointed half of it in gel containing sodium chloride, phenolphthalein and potassium ferricyanide, it will develop a pink area around the copper plated portion and a blue area around the bare iron half (54). The colors become more intense with time. This shows that iron continues to corrode as an anode, and, at the same time, there is an increasing concentration of alkali at the copper cathode.

When an iron nail with zinc plated on the pointed end is placed in the same gel, the iron now acts as a cathode and the zinc as an anode

(55). Accordingly, the red color identifying the cathode develops at the iron half. No iron goes into solution on this area, and, therefore, no blue color develops. The zinc corrodes as an anode at the point and is consumed in providing protection to the iron. A white area develops around the zinc because the zinc corrosion products form a white substance in contact with the potassium ferricyanide.

A similar technique may be used to show a local action cell on a single metal surface by placing an ordinary iron nail in a prepared gel (56). After a short time, a pink area develops around the shank of the nail, indicating formation of a cathode. Blue areas develop around the cold worked head and point of the nail where the iron goes into solution, indicating that these areas are the anodes. So we have shown again that corrosion on a single metal surface is electrochemical and is caused by a flow of current between anodic and cathodic areas.

As we observed previously with the zinc plated nail, the iron was made to act only as a cathode, and its anodic action was suppressed by the flow of current to it from the zinc. This is a simple example of cathodic protection, which can be illustrated further by similar experiments. In the first case, we use zinc joined electrically to an iron nail as the source of the protective current which makes the iron act as a cathode all over, as evidenced by the development of the red color showing the presence of the cathodic alkali. Note the absence of any blue color on the specimen receiving current from the zinc (57).

Likewise, cathodic protection can eliminate destructive galvanic action as between the steel and copper in a partially copper plated nail (58). We see that both the steel and copper are made cathodic and no anodic corrosion of the iron occurs in the composite specimen which receives current from the zinc. Full development of this color requires several hours.

In practice, the protective current may be impressed from a generator-rectifier or other external source through an appropriate anode, or it may be generated by corrosion of zinc as in the preceding experiments or of magnesium.[16]

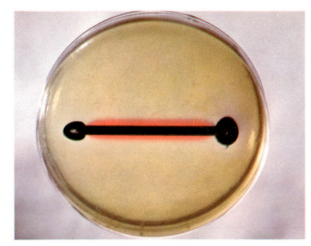

(56) Location of local anodes and cathode on a single iron nail.

(57) Cathodic protection of iron nail by zinc. Uncoupled nail shows blue coloration denoting presence of active corrosion on nail without protection.

(58) Cathodic protection of a nail partially plated with copper. Unprotected nail for comparison.

Passivity and Protective Films

The effect of oxygen on corrosion is variable and complex. We can see that it increases corrosion by acting as an electron acceptor and removing the film of hydrogen at a cathode (59). In higher concentration, oxygen can also retard corrosion. Oxygen, or oxidizing agents such as nitric acid, can form invisible protective films of their own and in this manner reduce corrosive action. The metal is said to have been rendered passive.[17] When some active metals become passive, they take on many features of the noble metals. For instance, iron made passive by an oxygen layer or oxide film approaches the noble potential of platinum and resists corrosion. The fact, too, is easily demonstrated. Iron is active in hydrochloric acid. When we couple it galvanically to platinum and then measure the potential difference in hydrochloric acid, we find this potential to be about 700 millivolts. If we make the measurement in concentrated nitric acid, in which iron becomes passive, we find that the potential difference between iron and platinum has dropped to about 300 millivolts.

However, the frail film responsible for the passivity of the iron in this case is easily damaged. For illustration, if we make a piece of iron passive by immersing it in nitric acid, a protective film formed by the nitric acid prevents corrosive

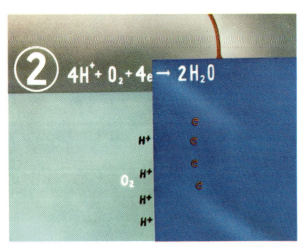

(59) *Cathodic reaction: Reduction of oxygen to form water.*

action. If we dip this passivated iron into copper sulfate, no plating out of copper occurs but a "light tap" is sufficient to rupture the passive film (60). The iron becomes active again. Copper plates out radially from the point where the film is broken. An active area at the point of impact

(60) *Rupture of passive film on iron.*

becomes anodic to the surrounding passive area acting as a cathode. The reducing action at the cathode destroys passivity and corrosive action spreads. This type of unstable passive film is obviously not a dependable means for protecting iron against corrosion.

Fortunately, by alloying iron with chromium or a combination of chromium and nickel, it can be given a much more stable passivity, such as we have in the familiar stainless steels. Whether these chromium alloys are active or passive depends upon their composition and their environment. For example, iron with 3 per cent of chromium is active in copper sulfate solution and plates out copper. With 6 per cent chromium, the plating out is proceeding more slowly but it is still active. When the alloy contains about 12 per cent or more of chromium, it achieves substantial passivity, and will resist corrosion in many environments, and, of course, the 18 per cent chromium-8 per cent nickel stainless steel is also passive in copper sulfate, as it is in nitric acid and many other corrosive media. This passivity is substantial and cannot be destroyed by striking the specimen with a glass rod such as occurred with the ordinary steel specimen treated in this way.

As happens with iron, the change from passivity to activity also changes the potential of stainless steel. In its fully active state, 18-8 stainless steel acts like iron and has about the same potential. A piece of 18-8 stainless steel and a piece of carbon steel may be immersed in warm sulfuric acid and joined through a millivoltmeter to measure their difference in potential. At the start the stainless steel is passive and shows a potential of 700 millivolts more noble than the carbon steel (61). The carbon steel is then brought into direct contact with the stainless steel (62). Hydrogen now forms on the stainless steel surface and destroys the film responsible for its passivity and its noble potential. When we take the piece of carbon

(62) Destruction of passive film on stainless steel by contact with carbon steel while in warm sulfuric acid.

steel away, we find that the potential difference between the stainless steel and the carbon steel has fallen towards zero (63). Now let us introduce another piece of the same stainless steel which is still passive. We see that the potential difference between this passive stainless steel is now as great as we just observed between ordinary steel and the passive stainless steel (64).

We can restore the passivity of the activated stainless steel by introducing nitric acid which has a strong passivating effect (65). The evolution of hydrogen on the activated stainless steel stops, and the potential drops toward zero. If we substitute a piece of platinum for the stainless steel that was always passive, we would now observe only a small difference in potential. This shows that the once active stainless steel has regained its passivity and its noble potential.

Difference in potential will occur when active and passive areas develop on the same piece of stainless steel. For example, the passivity of stainless steel depends upon a protective film of oxide

(61) Potential of 700 millivolts between passive stainless steel (left) and carbon steel (right) while in warm sulfuric acid.

(63) *Low potential difference between carbon steel and active stainless steel in warm sulfuric acid.*

or oxygen, which while not visible, is nevertheless very real, and this film must have an ample supply of oxygen to maintain it. Should the supply of oxygen at any point on the metal surface be insufficient to maintain passivity, for example, as a result of local shielding, a small local active area would develop, creating a large potential difference between it and the surrounding passive area (66). The result would be galvanic action between the small active area as the anode, and the large

(65) *Reduction in potential between active and passive stainless steel in warm sulfuric acid by addition of nitric acid to passify the active stainless specimen.*

(64) *Potential of 700 millivolts between active and passive stainless steel in warm sulfuric acid.*

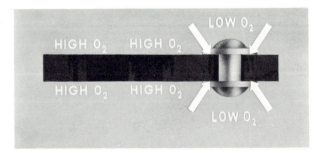

(66) *Active and passive areas on stainless steel with oxygen shielding leading to the active condition.*

surrounding passive area as cathode, with intense corrosive action at the small active area, the anode.

The development of these so-called active-passive cells causes corrosion in crevices where passivity has been destroyed[6] (67). We can make a practical demonstration of the damage that re-

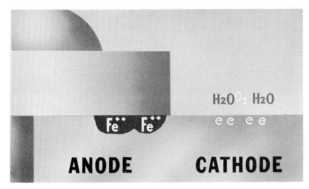

(67) *Location of anode and cathode areas because of oxygen starvation in crevice.*

sults from the breaking down of a protective film and the creation of active-passive cells. For example, let us observe the effect of a rubber band around a piece of stainless steel which is immersed in a dilute solution of sodium chloride and ferric chloride (68). After a period of time, we can see the rubber cutting into the edge of the steel. Oxygen cannot easily penetrate beneath the rubber band. Oxygen starvation causes the passivity to break down, creating an active area or anode beneath the rubber band; while the remainder of the

surface, being freely exposed to the dissolved oxygen, acts as a cathode. Obviously, with passive metals or alloys, it is necessary to avoid any deposits or crevices into which oxygen cannot penetrate. An example of how such harmful crevices occur in practice is provided by a specimen withdrawn from sea water. Plastic washers were used to insulate the fastenings on stainless steel test plates. Removal of the fastening and washer reveals that severe corrosion of the type discussed has occurred in the crevice that existed under the washer (69). Similar crevice corrosion resulting from active-passive cells can occur under many kinds of deposits or attachments, including the barnacles that grow on metals in sea water. These examples illustrate how important it is to keep stainless steels free from oxygen shielding deposits if we are to secure the full advantage of their most useful corrosion resisting properties.

Unlike the invisible films we have just discussed, thick films, such as rust, can be seen with the naked eye. Rust is a product of destructive action, but it may also have a protective value although the mechanism of that protection is different from that of the passive films on stainless steel. With thick films, such as rust formed on iron or low alloy steels exposed to the atmosphere, penetration of oxygen and water to the metal surface is retarded. Hence, the rate of corrosion diminishes as the rust becomes more impervious. But, there is a big dif-

(68) *Crevice corrosion of stainless steel under a rubber band when immersed in a chloride solution.*

(69) *Severe crevice corrosion under washer and fastening holding a test specimen while immersed in sea water.*

(70) Specimens undergoing atmospheric corrosion tests at Kure Beach, North Carolina.

(71) Appearance of rust on steels with different resistance to atmospheric corrosion. Left: Low copper steel. Center: Ordinary steel. Right: Nickel-copper-chromium steel.

ference in the nature of the rusts that develop on steels of different composition. The rusts have different colors and textures as can be seen from the appearance of some of the thousands of specimens undergoing atmospheric corrosion tests at the INCO Marine Test Station at Kure Beach, N. C. (70). Steels that show poor resistance to corrosion form heavy voluminous rusts that offer little resistance to the penetration of moisture as in the case of the specimen exposed only two years at Kure Beach (72).

(72) Voluminous rust formed on steel with low resistance to atmospheric corrosion.

Differences in the rate of progress of corrosion are illustrated by the behavior of three steels (71). At the left is a steel of exceptionally low copper content. The one in the middle is an ordinary steel, and the one at the right is a nickel-copper-chromium steel. Notice the progress of rusting of these three steels during their exposure at Kure Beach for three years (73). The differences are due primarily to differences in the protective qualities of their rusts as a result of the addition of "alloying elements," as shown by the "weight loss" vs. "time curves" for these three steels (74). They all corrode at about the same rate at the start; but as the more protective rust develops on the nickel steel, its rate of weight loss diminishes considerably, while the rate remains practically constant on the ordinary steel and actually increases a little on the steel of very low copper content.[18] Other materials, of course, are even

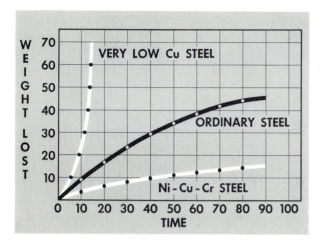

(74) Progress of corrosion on steels with different resistance to atmospheric corrosion. Left: Low copper steel. Center: Ordinary steel. Right: Nickel-copper-chromium steel.

(73) Corrosion of steels in marine atmosphere. Left: Low copper steel. Center: Ordinary steel. Right: Nickel-copper-chromium steel.

better than the low alloy steels in resisting atmospheric corrosion. For example, some panels of 18-8 chromium-nickel-stainless steel that have been exposed for over ten years still retain their original finish and continue to reflect the blue of the sky (75). Notice also, how the Monel alloy racks holding all these specimens have developed only a uniform superficial tarnish (78). Complete resistance to corrosion is illustrated by the complex nickel-chromium-molybdenum alloy known as Hastelloy C that continues to serve as a mirror after exposure on the racks at Kure Beach for ten years without any repolishing or cleaning (76).

The more we study corrosion, the more we realize two important facts. First, that corrosion is a natural process that occurs whenever there exists in an electrolyte a difference in the electrical potential of separate metals, or a potential difference between separate points on a single metal surface. Second, that corrosion can be controlled and avoided when we understand the conditions that cause corrosion currents to flow. When we understand these conditions, we know what action to take. We can, for example, choose the right materials for a given environment; that is, metals that do not develop damaging differences in potential. Sometimes this choice is obvious or it may require the advice of an expert as in a large chemical plant using different alloys selected for particular purposes (79).

(75) Stainless steel in a marine atmosphere reflecting the blue of the sky after ten years' exposure.

(76) Mirror finish on Hastelloy C after ten years of exposure in marine atmosphere.

Sometimes, we can adjust the environment to prolong the life of equipment that already exists such as by the addition of a chemical inhibitor to automobile radiators to prevent rusting. Inhibitors render the environment non-reactive or provide one that forms protective films.[19] Hu-

(78) Superficial tarnish on Monel nickel-copper alloy racks in marine atmosphere.

midity control of an atmosphere, as in shops handling delicate mechanisms, or in the storage of machine parts, is frequently an effective device.[20]

We can apply an electric current to counteract the natural corrosion currents, a remedy called cathodic protection[16] (77). We can give the metal a protective coating of paint[21], fabric, or some other more corrosion resistant metal.[22] We can develop new alloys to meet a given situation, alloys such as the Monel nickel-copper alloys, Inconel nickel-chromium alloys, Cupro-Nickels, Nickel-Silvers and the stainless steels. We can design and construct equipment free from built-in opportunities for corrosion currents to flow, as by avoiding crevices.[23]

Yes, what we understand, we can often control,

(77) Cathodic protection provided with magnesium anode.

and when we control corrosion, we are helping to save millions of dollars every year in damaged machinery. We are helping to conserve our natural resources by making metals last longer. We are even helping to save human lives by reducing accidents due to failure of corroded parts. This is a serious aspect of corrosion that is often overlooked. Equally important is the fact that reducing corrosion has tremendously aided the creation of many of our great industries. It has assisted old established industries to new heights of success. For many pure products we consider necessities today could not be made without the virtual elimination of corrosion in their manufacturing processes.

We have seen that, like a doctor, the student of corrosion principles has at his disposal, a considerable number of effective remedies. It is true that much still remains to be learned, but it is also true that if the corrosion principles and remedies already known were applied on a universal scale as they should be and could be, the standards of living would increase and all of us would benefit. It seems reasonable to suppose that, as progress is made in this field, future developments will be in the direction of facilitating selection of the most resistant members of the metal family to do the jobs for which they possess the greatest natural advantages. Not only the right metal, but the right one used in the right way in the right place. This discussion will have amply fulfilled its purpose if it has impressed you with the scientific reasonableness and desirability of this point of view as the goal of corrosion research.

(79) Corrosion resisting alloys are necessary in complex equipment for modern chemical processes.

(Above) Corrosion test specimens on rack being lifted from sea water.

(Below) Facilities on wharf at Harbor Island, N. C., for corrosion tests in sea water.

The late Dr. William F. Clapp who, for years, was a leader in our fight against corrosion and other forms of deterioration of materials.

Experiments

PURPOSE:

To demonstrate the importance of oxygen in the corrosion of iron in water

APPARATUS AND MATERIALS:

One tank or lecture bottle of oxygen
One tank or lecture bottle of nitrogen
Two 500-ml. Erlenmeyer flasks
Two 10 inch lengths of 6-8 mm. glass tubing
Suitable lengths of rubber tubing
Distilled water previously deaerated by boiling
Mineral spirits or benzene
Acetone
Iron Turnings

PROCEDURE:

Pour 250 ml. distilled water into each of the 500 ml. Erlenmeyer flasks. Using the lengths of glass tubing as bubblers, connect one to a source of nitrogen and allow it to bubble through the distilled water in one of the flasks. Similarly, allow oxygen to bubble through distilled water in the second flask. Degrease the iron turnings by rinsing first with benzene or mineral spirits, and then acetone. After rapid drying, preferably in a stream of clean air, weigh two 50 gram samples and introduce into the flasks containing distilled water. Continue bubbling the gases through their respective flasks and observe the development of rust during a period of several hours.

PURPOSE:

To illustrate the range of activity of metals

APPARATUS AND MATERIALS:

Four 400-ml. beakers
Distilled water
Concentrated nitric acid
Concentrated hydrochloric acid
One piece of iron or carbon steel in sheet form
One piece of platinum foil
Potassium
One pair forceps
Small pocket knife

PROCEDURE:

(a) Pour 250 ml. distilled water in one beaker. Then, immerse a piece of platinum foil of convenient size in the water. Repeat the experiment using a small strip of iron or carbon steel of convenient size and allow the metal to remain immersed overnight.

(b) Pour 250 ml. distilled water in a second beaker. Then, using forceps to handle the potassium (WARNING—DO NOT TOUCH POTASSIUM WITH BARE HANDS), cut a piece *no larger than a split pea* with the pocket knife. Then, taking proper precautions to protect eyes against spatter, drop the small piece of potassium in the beaker of water.

(c) Pour 250 ml. concentrated hydrochloric acid into a third beaker. Immerse a small piece of platinum foil and note the absence of any reaction. Repeat the experiment using a strip of iron or carbon steel and note the moderate reaction as made evident by the evolution of hydrogen.

(d) Pour 50 ml. distilled water into a fourth beaker. Add 200 ml. concentrated nitric acid and stir with a glass stirring rod. Then, immerse a piece of platinum foil in the diluted nitric acid and note the lack of action. Repeat the experiment with a strip of iron or carbon steel, but do not allow the sample to remain in the acid very long. (The violent action may be effectively stopped by plunging the iron or steel into water or by rinsing it in running water.)

PURPOSE:

To illustrate the displacement of an ion in solution by a more active metal as predicted by the Electromotive Series.

APPARATUS AND MATERIALS:

Four 400 ml. beakers
Copper sulfate, 5% solution
Hydrochloric acid, 10% solution
Silver nitrate, 5% solution
One strip of iron or carbon steel
One strip of zinc
One strip of copper
Distilled water

PROCEDURE:

(a) Pour 250 ml. 5% copper sulfate solution in a 400 ml. beaker. Immerse a strip of iron or carbon steel and note the deposition of copper on that part of the strip that has been immersed.

(b) Immerse a strip of zinc in 10% hydrochloric acid. Note the vigorous evolution of hydrogen as the zinc corrodes and displaces it from solution. Remove the strip of zinc from the acid and note the etched condition of its surface resulting from the corrosion.

(c) Immerse a strip of copper in 10% hydrochloric acid and note the absence of any reaction. Copper is below hydrogen in the Electromotive Series and does not displace hydrogen.

(d) Immerse a strip of copper in 5% silver nitrate solution and note the deposition of silver on the copper surface. Copper is above silver in the Electromotive Series and displaces silver from solution, at the same time, suffering an equivalent amount of corrosion.

PURPOSE:

To demonstrate the driving force in galvanic corrosion or the potential developed between dissimilar metals in a galvanic couple.

APPARATUS AND MATERIALS:

3% sodium chloride solution
One strip of sheet zinc, 1″ x 6″ or other convenient size
One strip of sheet aluminum
One strip of sheet copper
One large beaker or jar to accommodate two of the strips
One millivoltmeter, 0-1000 mv. D. C.
Wire leads and clips for connecting strips to millivoltmeter

PROCEDURE:

(a) Fill the beaker or jar with 3% sodium chloride solution. Suspend the strips of zinc and aluminum in the solution and connect them to the millivoltmeter, making sure that the connecting wires are not in the solution or wetted by it. Observe the voltage indicated by the meter.

(b) Repeat the experiment using zinc and copper strips. Again note the voltage and observe that it is greater than in the case of the zinc-aluminum couple. Also, observe that this potential decreases with time as a result of polarization of the copper by the current that flows through the circuit.

Influence of Cathode Area in Galvanic Corrosion

PURPOSE:

To demonstrate the influence of area of the cathode materials on the magnitude of galvanic corrosion.

APPARATUS AND MATERIALS:

Two 800-ml. beakers
Two strips of carbon steel, 2″ x 6″

One piece of sheet copper, ½″ x 3″
One piece of sheet copper, 6″ x 8″, rolled to fit into beaker
Two milliammeters, 0-100 ma.
Wire for connecting milliammeters to metal strips
Sodium chloride solution, 3%
Oxygen in convenient lecture bottles or tank
Glass tubing, 6-8 mm., to use as a gas bubbler
Rubber tubing, to connect bubbler to oxygen bottle or tank

PROCEDURE:

(a) Place the beakers side by side and arrange glass tube bubblers in each beaker so that the flow of oxygen may be controlled. Fill each beaker with 3% sodium chloride solution. Suspend a steel strip and the small copper strip in one beaker and bubble oxygen through the solution. After one or two minutes, connect the specimens to a milliammeter, steel to the negative terminal and copper to the positive. Note the initial value of the current and at several intervals over a ten-minute period.

(b) Repeat the experiment in the second beaker using the large copper sheet and the second steel strip. Again note the initial value of the current and at several intervals over a ten-minute period.

(c) Now stop the flow of oxygen through the solution in the two beakers and record the current in each case at half-minute intervals over a ten-minute period.

(d) Restore the flow of oxygen and record the currents at intervals over a five-minute period.

Corrosion in Metal Ion Concentration Cells

PURPOSE:

To demonstrate that ion concentration gradients in a solution covering a metal surface can generate corrosion currents between the metal areas in contact with the solution of different concentrations.

APPARATUS AND MATERIALS:

Two 600-ml. beakers
600 ml., 0.001% copper sulfate solution
600 ml., 10% copper sulfate solution
Concentrated sulfuric acid
Two strips of copper, 2″ x 8″, of convenient thickness
One U-tube or Y-tube to form a salt bridge between solutions in beakers
Agar agar
One microammeter, 0-1000 microamperes
One millivoltmeter, 0-200 mv.
Wire and clamps to connect copper strips to meters

PROCEDURE:

(a) Fill the salt bridge U-tube with a gel containing copper sulfate. This may be done as follows: Disperse 1.5 gms. agar agar, by boiling in 50 ml. 10% copper sulfate solution. Then fill the U-tube with the hot dispersion of agar agar in 10% $CuSO_4$ solution. Allow it to cool and set as a gel. Invert the U-tube allowing the arms to hang over the edges of the two beakers.

(b) Fill one beaker with 10% copper sulfate solution and the other beaker with 0.001% copper sulfate solution, each solution having been previously acidified with sulfuric acid to about 10% acid. Suspend a strip of clean copper in each beaker and connect them to a microammeter. Note the current generated by the copper strips in solution with different copper ion concentrations. Then connect the millivoltmeter and record the potential difference developed by the copper strips in solutions of different copper ion concentration. Note the direction of current and in which concentration the corrosion is proceeding as a result of the current.

(c) Dilute 60 ml. 10% copper sulfate solution to 600 ml. with distilled water, and adjust the total acid concentration to 10% by adding the proper amount of sulfuric acid. Then repeat experiment (b) using 1% and 0.001% copper sulfate solutions in the two beakers.* Again note and record the current and voltage generated by the copper strips in these two solutions.

(d) By successive ten-fold dilutions of the 1% copper sulfate solution, repeat experiment (c) with 0.001% copper sulfate solution together with 0.1%, 0.01% and 0.001% solutions.* Note and record the current and voltage generated in each instance.

(e) Plot current and potential vs. ratio of copper ion concentration, in experiments (b) and (d).

*Note. The total sulfuric acid concentration in each solution should be identical, namely, 10% as used. The concentration of copper sulfate is the only variable.

Corrosion in Oxygen Concentration Cells

PURPOSE:

To demonstrate that an oxygen concentration gradient in a solution covering a metal surface can generate corrosion currents between the metal areas in contact with the solution of different concentrations

APPARATUS AND MATERIALS:
Two 600-ml. beakers
1200 ml. 3% sodium chloride solution, previously deaerated by boiling
Two strips of low carbon steel, 2" x 8", of convenient thickness
One U-tube to form a salt bridge between solutions in the beakers
Agar Agar
One microammeter, 0-200 microamperes range
Wire and clamps to connect steel strips to meters

PROCEDURE:

Fill the salt bridge U-tube with a gel containing 3% sodium chloride. This may be done as follows: Disperse 1.5 gms. agar agar by boiling in 50 ml. 3% sodium chloride solution. Then fill the U-tube with the hot dispersion, allow it to cool and set as a gel. Invert the U-tube allowing the arms to hang over the edges of the two beakers. Then fill the beakers to the same level being sure that contact is made with the solution at both ends of the salt bridge. Suspend a freshly abraded steel strip in each beaker and connect them to a microammeter. Note the existence of a small current because of slight differences in the two solutions. This current can be reduced to zero by slight movement of one or the other steel strip as determined by trial. After the current has thus been reduced to zero, bubble oxygen through the solution in one beaker and nitrogen through the other. Note the current that is generated after the gases have bubbled through the solutions for a few minutes. Note the direction of the current and which steel strip is suffering corrosion as a result of the current.

Color Reactions of Phenolphthalein and Potassium Ferricyanide

PURPOSE:

To demonstrate the color reactions of the indicators, phenolphthalein and potassium ferricyanide.

APPARATUS AND MATERIALS:

One small bottle containing a 5% potassium ferricyanide solution
One small bottle containing a 1% alcohol solution of phenolphthalein
1% sodium hydroxide solution
Distilled water
5% solution ferrous chloride
Three 250-ml. beakers

PROCEDURE:

(a) Pour 100 ml. 1% sodium hydroxide solution into a 250 ml. beaker. Note its color. Then add a few drops of 1% alcohol solution of phenolphthalein and stir. Again note the color.

(b) Pour 100 ml. distilled water into a 250 ml. beaker. Note the color. Then add a few drops of the potassium ferricyanide solution, and again note the color. Save this for comparison in part (c).

(c) Pour 100 ml. distilled water into another beaker and add a few ml. of ferrous chloride solution. Then add a few drops of potassium ferricyanide solution and note the color. Compare this with the results in part (b).

Anodes and Cathodes in Corrosion Reactions

PURPOSE:

To show the existence and location of anodes and cathodes in corrosion processes.

APPARATUS AND MATERIALS:

Agar agar gel containing 3% sodium chloride
5% potassium ferricyanide solution
1% phenolphthalein solution
Three iron nails
Three iron nails with point half copper plated
One iron nail with point half plated with zinc
One milliammeter, 0-10 ma., D. C., range
Two strips of thin sheet zinc, ½" x 6" x .04" (approximate)
Wires and clamps for connecting nails and zinc strips to milliammeter
Three or more Petri dishes large enough to accommodate nails (about 50-60 mm. diameter)

PROCEDURE:

(a) Prepare 250 ml. agar agar gel containing 3% sodium chloride. To do this, dissolve 7.5 gms. sodium chloride in 250 ml. distilled water. Add 5 gms. powdered agar agar and boil the mixture until the agar is dispersed. Then add 5 ml. of the potassium ferricyanide solution and 1 ml. of the phenolphthalein solution.

(b) To demonstrate the accumulation of alkali at cathode areas and corrosion at anode areas, fill a Petri dish with the hot gel solution and allow to cool without disturbance until it begins to set. At this point place one of the partially copper plated nails in the gel and observe the subsequent color developments over a period of several hours. The red color develops along the copper surface because it is performing as a cathode and the blue color develops on the bare iron surface that is the anode in the copper-iron galvanic couple. The red color results from the accumulation of alkali on cathode areas and the blue color reveals the presence of ferrous ions at the iron anode surface. Save for comparison with experiment (f).

(c) Repeat experiment (b) using a nail that is partially plated with zinc. Note the color development over several hours. In this instance no blue

coloration appears because zinc is more active than iron and performs as the anode in the zinc-iron galvanic couple. Zinc ions form at the anode but they do not form a colored compound with the indicators used. Hence, no color develops on the zinc area.

(d) To demonstrate the existence of and to locate anodes and cathodes on a single metal surface, repeat experiment (b) using a plain bare iron nail. Note the development of blue and red colors at different places on the nail. (Most frequently the blue color develops on the cold worked head and point while the red develops on the shank.) Save for comparison with the results in experiment (e).

(e) To demonstrate the role of galvanic anodes in cathodic protection, solder a wire connection onto the head of a bare iron nail and clip a second wire on a strip of zinc. Bend the zinc strip so that it will rest in a Petri dish without support. Connect the nail and strip of zinc to a milliammeter. Then pour warm gel solution into a Petri dish and allow to cool as in experiment (b). As the gel begins to set, place the nail and zinc strip in the gel. Note that iron is not corroding and forming iron ions. The development of a red color on the iron surface shows that it is now acting entirely as a cathode. (A local red coloration that may develop on the zinc strip where it comes out of the gel is due to a secondary oxygen concentration cell effect on the zinc. This is to be distinguished from the reactions of the zinc-iron nail galvanic couple.) Compare with the results of experiment (d).

(f) To demonstrate that galvanic anodes through cathodic protection may also eliminate destructive galvanic corrosion, repeat experiment (e) using a partially copper plated nail in place of the bare iron nail. Compare the results with those of experiment (b). Note again that a red color develops on the nail receiving protection from the sacrificial zinc anode.

Passive Film on Iron

PURPOSE:

To demonstrate the corrosion resistance and nobility of iron when in the passive condition.

APPARATUS AND MATERIALS:

One D. C. millivoltmeter, 0-1000 mv.
One strip iron, approximately 1/16" x 2" x 8"
One strip iron, approximately 1/16" x 2" x 3"
One strip platinum, foil or sheet, 1" x 2" or larger
Hydrochloric acid, 6 normal
Nitric acid, concentrated

Distilled water
Copper sulfate solution, 10%
Wires with suitable clips to connect metals to millivoltmeter
Three 1000-ml. beakers
Two glass rods

PROCEDURE:

(a) Fill a beaker with hydrochloric acid. Suspend a large strip of iron and the platinum strip in the acid. Connect them to the millivoltmeter, taking care not to allow the wires or clips to contact the acid. Note and record the voltage generated by the couple. The iron is active in hydrochloric acid.

(b) Repeat experiment (a) using concentrated nitric acid in place of the hydrochloric acid. (CAUTION—THE NITRIC ACID MUST NOT BE DILUTED!) Note that the generated voltage is much smaller because the concentrated nitric acid has formed a passive film on the iron rendering it more noble.

(c) Arrange three beakers in a row and fill them respectively with concentrated nitric acid, distilled water and copper sulfate solution. Then drill a small hole in one end of the small iron specimen and in the end of one of the glass rods make a small hook from which the iron specimen can be suspended. Then using this hook, completely immerse the iron specimen in the concentrated nitric acid and hold it there without shaking or other mechanical disturbance for about 30 seconds. Then, being extremely careful to avoid shaking or other disturbance of a mechanical nature, slowly remove the specimen from the nitric acid, rinse in the distilled water and then immerse in the copper sulfate solution. Immediately raise the sample from the solution and note that copper has not plated out on the iron that has been passivated in the nitric acid. Now lightly tap the suspended iron with the second glass rod and observe the deposition of copper as the passive film is ruptured by the mechanical shock. Also, note that the deposition of copper starts at the point on the surface where the passive film is ruptured and spreads from this point over the entire surface.

In conducting this experiment use extraordinary care not to jar or shake the specimen between the time it is removed from the nitric acid and when it is finally tapped with the glass rod. The film responsible for the passivity is very fragile and is ruptured by the slightest mechanical shock. Furthermore, this experiment should be conducted in a room that is relatively free of hydrochloric acid fumes since these may also destroy the delicate passive film before the sample is tapped.

Oxygen Concentration Cells in Water Droplets

PURPOSE:

To reveal the location of the anode and cathode areas when corrosion of steel occurs under a single drop of water.

APPARATUS AND MATERIALS:

Agar agar dispersion in sodium chloride solution containing potassium ferricyanide and phenol-phthalein
Small piece of sheet iron or carbon steel, approximately 1.5″ x 1.5″

PROCEDURE:

(a) Prepare a gel mixture for use in experiment (b) as described in experiment (a) under Anodes and Cathodes in Corrosion Reactions.

(b) Clean the piece of iron or carbon steel by abrasion with emery cloth. Then place on the clean surface a drop of the gel mixture (about 1/4″ diameter) and note the development of colors. Oxygen is more accessible to the steel at the periphery of the drop rendering it more noble than the steel at the center. Hence, a cathode develops around the outer edge of the drop and produces a red color. The anode at the center corrodes forming ferrous ions that react with the potassium ferricyanide to form a blue color in the center.

Passivating Influence of Chromium in Steel

PURPOSE:

To demonstrate the passivation of steel by alloying it with chromium or chromium and nickel.

APPARATUS AND MATERIALS:

One piece of carbon steel sheet of convenient size, e. g. 2″ x 8″
One piece of 3% chromium steel
One piece of 6% chromium steel
One piece of 12% chromium steel
One piece of 18% chromium-12% nickel steel
One beaker, 600 ml.
10% copper sulfate solution

PROCEDURE:

(a) Immerse successively in the copper sulfate solution the above materials and note that copper plates out on the carbon steel, 3% chromium steel, and 6% chromium steel, but not on the 12% chromium or the 18-8 chromium-nickel steels. Also note that the deposition of copper on the 6% chromium steel takes place at a slower rate than on the carbon steel and 3% chromium steel.

(b) Reimmerse the 12% chromium steel in the copper sulfate, remove it and then tap it with a glass rod as in part (c) of the preceding experiment. Note that the strongly passive condition resulting from the presence of 12% chromium cannot be destroyed by mechanical shock as in the case of carbon steel or iron.

(c) Repeat part (b) with 18-8 chromium nickel steel noting that its passivity also cannot be destroyed by simple mechanical shock.

Crevice Corrosion

PURPOSE:

To demonstrate the development of corrosion in crevices because of oxygen concentration differential.

APPARATUS AND MATERIALS:

One strip of 12% chromium steel, AISI Type 410, 2″ x 8″
Two pieces of wood, ⅛″ x ½″ x 1″ (approximate)
One rubber band, ⅛″ wide and sufficiently long to stretch 8″
One 400 ml. beaker
3% solution of sodium chloride
5% ferric chloride solution

PROCEDURE:

Fill the 400 ml. beaker with sodium chloride solution and add a few ml. of the ferric chloride solution. Then, place the rubber band around the stainless steel specimen so that it is parallel to the long dimension of the sample. Place wood "bridges" under the rubber band on each side of and at the center of the specimen. This will provide a crevice at the ends of the specimen under the rubber band but not on the flat surfaces.

Suspend this assembly in the solution so that the lower edge does not rest on the bottom of the beaker and set aside for occasional inspection over a six to eight-week period. During this period, it may be necessary to replace water that has evaporated. It is also desirable to renew the solution about twice a week after corrosion has begun.

Note the development of localized corrosion in the area where the rubber band is in contact with the stainless steel.

Active and Passive Conditions of Stainless Steel

PURPOSE:

To demonstrate the active and passive electrode potentials of stainless steel.

APPARATUS AND MATERIALS:

2 strips 18-8 chromium-nickel stainless steel, 1½″ x 6″ (approximately)
1 strip carbon steel, 1½″ x 6″
1 strip of platinum sheet or foil
Sulfuric acid, concentrated
Nitric acid, concentrated
Distilled water
Millivoltmeter, 0-1000 mv. D. C.
Wires and suitable clips to connect samples to millivoltmeter
One 1000 ml. beaker
One 250 ml. beaker

PROCEDURE:

(a) Pour approximately 600 ml. distilled water in the 1000 ml. beaker. Then add slowly and carefully with constant stirring 150 ml. concentrated sulfuric acid. This mixing generates considerable heat and must be done carefully. While the dilute acid is still hot, suspend in the acid, so that they do not touch each other, one strip of carbon steel and one of 18-8 stainless steel. Note that the carbon steel is active and displaces hydrogen whereas the stainless steel is passive and does not displace hydrogen. Connect them to the millivoltmeter and note the voltage.

(b) Now, without removing either specimen from the acid and without disconnecting them from the voltmeter, bring the carbon steel into contact with the stainless steel below the surface of the acid. Notice that hydrogen is now generated on the stainless steel as well as on the carbon steel. Now separate the carbon steel from the stainless steel and note that the hydrogen evolution continues from both specimens. Also, note that the voltage is now much lower than before the two specimens were brought into contact with each other. The stainless steel is now as active as the carbon steel.

(c) Replace the carbon steel with a new piece of stainless steel and observe that this new piece is passive and does not generate hydrogen whereas the active stainless specimen does. Connect these to the millivoltmeter and note that the voltage between active and passive stainless is about the same as that noted in (a).

(d) Add 150 ml. concentrated nitric acid to the sulfuric acid after completing (c) and note the decrease in the potential between the active and passive samples of stainless steel. Also, note that the evolution of hydrogen on the active specimen ceases. The nitric acid has caused the active sample to become passive again.

Books on Corrosion and Its Prevention

I IN ENGLISH

1. Corrosion Resistance of Metals and Alloys—R. J. McKay and R. Worthington—American Chemical Society Monograph No. 71. Published by Reinhold Publishing Co., New York, New York, 1936.

2. Protective Films on Metals—E. S. Hedges, published by Chapman and Hall, London, 1937.

3. Soil Corrosion and Pipe Line Protection—Scott Ewing. Published by American Gas Association, New York, New York, 1938.

4. The Corrosion of Iron and Steel—J. C. Hudson. Published by Chapman and Hall, London, 1940.

5. Metallic Corrosion Passivity and Protection—U. R. Evans, published by Edward Arnold and Co., London, 1946. Longmans, Green and Co., New York.

6. The Corrosion Handbook, edited by H. H. Uhlig, sponsored by The Electrochemical Society, Inc., published by John Wiley and Sons, Inc., New York, New York, U. S. A.—1948.

7. Corrosion—Causes and Prevention. Third Edition, F. N. Speller. Published by McGraw-Hill Book Company, New York, New York, 1951.

8. Corrosion Testing Procedures—F. A. Champion, published by John Wiley and Sons, Inc., New York, New York, 1952.

9. Protective Coatings for Metals—R. M. Burns and W. W. Bradley—American Chemical Society, Monograph No. 129. Published by Reinhold Publishing Co., New York, 1955.

II IN GERMAN

1. Die Korrosion Metallischer Werkstoffe—O. Bauer, O. Krohnke and G. Masing. Published by S. Hirzel, Leipzig. 3 volumes—1936, 1938, 1940.

2. Zunderfeste Legierungen—W. Hessenbruck, Julius Springer, Berlin, 1940. (Reprinted by Edwards Bros., Inc.)

3. Mesung und Verhutung der Metallkorrosion—F. Todt. Published by Walter de Gruyter and Co., Berlin, 1941. Reprinted by Edwards Bros., Inc., Ann Arbor, Michigan.

4. Die Zerselzungserscheinungen der Metalle—G. Schikorr. Published by J. A. Barth, Leipzig, 1943—reprinted by Edwards Bros., Inc., Ann Arbor, Michigan.

III IN SPANISH

1. El Problema de la Corrosion Metalica—E. Jimeno. Published by Inst. Espanol de Oceanografia, Madrid, 1947.

References

1. COSTS OF CORROSION

a. F. A. Rohrman, "Economic Aspects of Corrosion Problems," Corrosion, 3, 67 (1947).

b. Harry E. Jordan, "Corrosion Costs to the Water Industry," Corrosion, 3, 367 (1947).

c. H. H. Anderson, "Corrosion Costs—Beader Report," Business Week, May 24, 1947, #925, 37-38.

d. M. C. Miller, "Cutting Corrosion Costs—The Billion Dollar Side Show," American Gas Association Monthly, 31, #9, pp. 28-29, 52 (1949).

e. J. F. Stephenson, "Costs and Savings Effected by Cathodic Protection for a Short Section of Line," Oil Gas J., 49, No. 20, pp. 240-241 (1950), Sept. 21.

f. R. B. Wilson, "Management's Attitude Toward a Corrosion Control Program," Gas Age, 106, Nov. 9, 1950, #10.

g. H. H. Uhlig, "Costs of Corrosion to the United States," Proc. U. N. Scient. Conf. on Conservation and Utilization of Resources, Vol. II, pp. 213-218 (1951).

h. W. H. J. Vernon, "The Costs of Corrosion and of its Control," Proc. U. N. Scient. Conf. on Conservation and Utilization of Resources, Vol. II, pp. 218-222 (1951).

i. F. K. Mitchell, "Control of Corrosion Damage to Rolling Stock Through Proper Design and Maintenance," Corrosion, 7, 269 (1951).

j. T. S. Crane, "Corrosion Problems of the Railroad," Corrosion, 8, 141-151 (1952).

2. TARNISHING

a. G. Tamann and W. Koster, "Velocity of Action of Oxygen, Hydrogen Sulfide and Halogens on Metals," Z. Anorg. Allgem. Chem., 123, 216 (1922).

b. N. B. Pilling and R. E. Bedworth, "The Oxidation of Metals at High Temperatures," J. Inst. Metals, 29, 534 (1923).

c. W. H. J. Vernon, "First (experimental) Report to the Atmospheric Corrosion Committee (British Non-Ferrous Metals Research Assn.)," Trans. Faraday Soc., 19, 839-900 (1923-1924).

d. W. H. J. Vernon, "Second (experimental) Report to the Atmospheric Corrosion Committee (British Non-Ferrous Metals Research Assn.)," Trans. Faraday Soc., 23, 113-183 (1927).

e. W. H. J. Vernon and L. Whitby, "The Open-Air Corrosion of Copper, A Chemical Study of the Surface Patina," J. Inst. Metals, 42, 181 (1929.)

f. W. H. J. Vernon and L. Whitby, "The Open-Air Corrosion of Copper, Part II—The Mineralogical Relationship of Corrosion Products," J. Inst. Metals, 44, 389 (1930).

g. W. H. J. Vernon, "Laboratory Study of the Atmospheric Corrosion of Metals, Part I—Corrosion of Copper in Certain Synthetic Atmospheres with Particular Reference to the Influence of Sulfur Dioxide in Air of Various Relative Humidities," Trans. Faraday Soc., 27, 255-77, 582 (1931).

h. W. H. J. Vernon, "The Fogging of Nickel," J. Inst. Metals, 48, 121-145 (1932).

i. W. H. J. Vernon, "The Open-Air Corrosion of Copper, Part III — Artificial Production of Green Patina," J. Inst. Metals, 49, 153-166 (1932).

j. C. Wagner, "The Mechanism of the Movement of Ions and Electrons in Solids and the Interpretation of Reactions Between Solids," Trans. Faraday Soc., 34, 851 (1938).

k. W. H. J. Vernon, E. I. Akeroyd and E. G. Stroud, "The Direct Oxidation to Zinc," J. Inst. Metals, 65, 301 (1939).

l. W. H. J. Vernon, "The Corrosion of Metals in Air," Chemistry and Industry, 21, 314-318 (1943).

m. U. R. Evans, "Mechanism of Oxidation and Tarnishing," Trans. Electrochem. Soc., 91, 547 (1947).

n. A. L. Simmons, "Tarnishing of Nickel-Silver," Metal Progress, 58, Sept. 1950, #3, pp. 345-347.

3. GALVANIC CORROSION

    a. F. L. LaQue and G. L. Cox, "Some Observations of the Potentials of Metals and Alloys in Sea Water," Proc. A.S.T.M., 40, 670 (1940).

    b. W. A. Wesley, "Controlling Factors in Galvanic Corrosion," Proc. A.S.T.M., 40, 690 (1940).

    c. G. W. Seagren, G. H. Young and F. L. LaQue, "The Effectiveness of Paint in Suppressing Galvanic Corrosion," Corrosion, 2, June 1946, #2, pp. 19-27.

    d. M. G. Fontana, "Corrosion," J. Ind. Eng. Chem., 39, #7, pp. 85A-86A (1947).

    e. Report of A.S.T.M. Sub-Comm. VIII on Galvanic and Electrolytic Corrosion, "Stainless Steels Coupled with Other Metals," Proc. A.S.T.M., 48, 167-175 (1948).

    f. G. T. Colegate, "Galvanic Corrosion and Its Practical Significance," Metal Treatment, 15, No. 56, pp. 183-192 (1948-1949).

    g. F. L. LaQue, "Galvanic Corrosion in Oil and Gas Well Fluids," Corrosion, 5, 86-9 (1949).

    h. F. L. LaQue and W. D. Mogerman, "Notes on Galvanic Corrosion," World Oil, 129, Oct. 1949, pp. 153-154, 158.

    i. S. B. Ashkinazy and J. M. Joyce, "Galvanic Corrosion—What It Is and How It Can Be Avoided," Materials and Methods, 31, #2, pp. 49-53 (1950).

    j. R. H. Brown, "Galvanic Corrosion," Amer. Gas J., 173 (1950), #6, pp. 26-30.

    k. H. D. Holler, "Studies on Galvanic Corrosion," Part I—J. Electrochem. Soc., 97, 271-282 (1950); Part II—J. Electrochem. Soc., 97, 453-461 (1950); Part III—J. Electrochem. Soc., 98, 252 (1951).

    l. F. L. LaQue, Edgar Marburg Lecture, "Corrosion Testing," Proc. A.S.T.M., 51, 495 (1951).

    m. M. E. Parker, "Bimetallic Corrosion," Oil and Gas J., 50, No. 13, p. 81, Aug. 2 (1951).

    n. K. M. Huston and R. B. Teel, "Some Observations of the Potentials of Stainless Steels in Flowing Sea Water," Corrosion, 8, 251 (1952).

4. PITTING

    a. H. H. Uhlig, "Pitting of Stainless Steels," Trans. Am. Inst. Mining Met Engr., 140, 411 (1940).

    b. C. Edelenau and U. R. Evans, "The Causes of Localized Character of Corrosion on Aluminum," Trans. Faraday Soc., 47, Oct. 1941, Pt. 10, pp. 1121-1135.

    c. H. H. Uhlig, "The Role of Nitrogen in 18-8 Stainless Steel," Trans. A.S.M., 30, 963 (1942).

    d. H. S. Campbell, "Pitting Corrosion in Copper Water Pipes Caused by Films of Carbonaceous Material Produced During Manufacture," J. Inst. Metals, 77, June 1950, Pt. 4, pp. 345-356.

    e. J. W. Matthews and H. H. Uhlig, "Sodium Hydroxide as Inhibitors of Pitting in 18-8 Stainless Steel," Corrosion, 7, 419-422 (1951).

    f. P. Ffield, "Some Aspects of Ship Bottom Corrosion," Corrosion, 8, 29-48, 69-88 (1952).

5. STRESS CORROSION CRACKING

    a. H. Moore, S. Beckinsale and Clarice E. Mallinson, "The Season-Cracking of Brass and Other Copper Alloys," J. Inst. Metals, 25, 37 (1921).

    b. S. L. Hoyt and M. A. Scheil, "Stress Corrosion Cracking in Austenitic Stainless Steels," Trans. A.S.M., 27, 191 (1939).

    c. J. C. Hodge and J. L. Miller, "Stress Corrosion Cracking of the Austenitic Chromium-Nickel Steels and Its Industrial Implications," Trans. A.S.M., 28, 25-82 (1940).

    d. E. Houdremont and H. Schrader, "Stress Cracking Caused by Hydrogen and Internal Stressing," Stahl und Eisen, 61, July 1941, #27, pp. 649-653.

    e. F. C. Althof, "Inter-and Intracrystalline Corrosion and Their Causes," Z. Metallkunde, 36, #8, pp. 177-186, (1944).

    f. A. S. T. M.—A. I. M. E. Symposium on Stress Corrosion Cracking—1944.

    g. J. T. Waber, H. J. MacDonald and B. Longtin, "Theory of Stress Corrosion Cracking of Mild Steel in Nitrate Solutions," Trans. Electrochem. Soc., 87, 209 (1944).

    h. H. H. Uhlig, "The Present Status of Knowledge on Stress Corrosion Cracking of Iron," Record of Chem. Progress, 8, Jan.-April, 1947, #1/2, pp. 21-23.

    i. W. P. Rees, "Note on Stress-Corrosion Cracking of Steels in the Presence of Sulfur Compounds—Paper #1104," Metals and Alloys, 1948, pp. 333-335, 463-484.

j. D. H. Thompson and A. W. Tracy, "Influence of Composition on the Stress-Corrosion Cracking of Some Copper-Base Alloys—TP2518E," Metal Ind., 74, Apr. 15, 1949, #15, pp. 286-293.

k. H. H. Uhlig, "Action of Corrosion and Stress on 13 Cr Stainless Steels," Metal Progress, 57, 486-487 (1950).

l. M. T. Simnad, "A Review of the Electro-chemistry of Stressed Metals," J. Electrochem. Soc., 97, pp. 31C-44C, #2 (1950).

m. J. J. Harwood, "The Influence of Stress on Corrosion," Corrosion, 6, 249-259, 290-307 (1950).

n. E. Franke, "The Influence of Internal Stresses on Corrosion," Werkstoffe und Korrosion, 1, Oct. 1950, pp. 404-412.

o. H. Nathorst, "Stress Corrosion Cracking of Stainless Steels," Welding Research Council Bulletin Series No. 6, October, 1950. Welding Research Council of the Engineering Foundation, New York.

6. CREVICE CORROSION

a. R. J. McKay, "Corrosion by Electrolytic Concentration Cells," Trans. Amer. Electrochem. Soc., 41, 201-215 (1922).

b. E. H. Wyche, L. R. Voigt and F. L. LaQue, "Corrosion in Crevices," Trans. Electrochem. Soc., Vol. 89, 265 (1946).

c. H. Endo, Science Rpts. of Res. Inst. Tohoku Univ., 1, Series A, No. 4, 349-356 (1949), December.

d. O. B. Ellis and F. L. LaQue, "Area Effects in Crevice Corrosion," Corrosion, 7, 362-364 (1951).

e. T. P. May and H. A. Humble, "Effectiveness of Cathodic Currents in Reducing Crevice Corrosion and Pitting of Several Materials in Sea Water," Corrosion, 8, 50-56 (1952).

7. SELECTIVE CORROSION OF ALLOYS

a. C. W. Stillwell and E. S. Turnipseed, "Mechanism of Dezincification," J. Ind. Eng., 26, 740 (1934).

b. H. L. Maxwell, "Cast Iron in Chemical Equipment," Mech. Eng., 58, No. 12, p. 803 (1936).

c. W. A. Wesley, H. R. Copson and F. L. LaQue, "Some Consequences of Graphitic Corrosion of Cast Iron," Metals and Alloys, 7, No. 12, p. 325 (1936).

d. W. Lynes, "Comparative Value of Arsenic, Antimony, and Phosphorus in Preventing Dezincification," Proc. A.S.T.M., 41, 859 (1941).

e. M. G. Fontana, "Pitting and Dezincification," J. Ind. Eng. Chem., 39, #5, 87A-88A (1947).

f. L. M. Leedom, "Graphitic Corrosion of Cast Iron," Corrosion, 3, #7, p. 30 (1947).

g. G. T. Colegate, "Dezincification", Metal. Ind., 73, Dec. 17, 1948, #25, pp. 483-485; #26, pp. 507-509; #27, pp. 531-533.

h. A. L. Simons, "Plug Dezincification in Cartridge Brass," Metal Progress, 57, 496 (1950).

8. Sir R. A. Hadfield, "Faraday and his Metallurgical Researches," The Penton Publishing Co., Cleveland, Ohio, pp. 90-137 (1932).

9. M. Faraday, "The Correlation of the Physical Forces," a lecture at the Royal Institution, reprinted in The Harvard Classics, Vol. 30, pp. 75-88. P. F. Collier and Son Company, New York, 1910.

10. I. A. Denison, "Contributions of Sir Humphry Davy to Cathodic Protection," Corrosion, 3, 295 (1947).

11. R. Adie, "An Account of Experiments with Galvanic Couples Immersed in Pure Water and in Oxygenated Water," Phil. Mag., 31, 350-356 (1947).

12. W. R. Whitney, "The Corrosion of Iron," J. Amer. Chem. Soc., 22, 394 (1903); reprinted in Corrosion, 3, 331 (1947).

13. CAUSES OF CORROSION

a. R. E. Wilson, "The Mechanism of Corrosion of Iron and Steel in Natural Waters and the Calculation of Specific Rates of Corrosion," J. Ind. Eng. Chem., 15, 127 (1923).

b. W. G. Whitman and R. P. Russell, "The Acid Corrosion of Metals," J. Ind. Eng. Chem., 17, 348 (1925).

c. U. R. Evans and T. P. Hoar, "The Velocity of Corrosion from the Electrochemical Standpoint, Part II," Proc. Roy. Soc. (A), 137, 343 (1932).

d. G. D. Bengough, U. R. Evans, T. P. Hoar, and F. Wormwell, "The Corrosion of Metals by Salt Solutions and Natural Waters: An Agreed Statement," Chem. Ind., p. 1043 (1938).

e. U. R. Evans, "Report on Corrosion Research Work at Cambridge University Interrupted by the Outbreak of War," J. Iron and Steel Inst., 141, 221P (1940).

f. R. B. Mears and R. H. Brown, "Causes of Corrosion Currents," J. Ind. Eng. Chem., 33, 1001 (1941).

14. T. P. Hoar, "The Study of Cathodic Reactions in Metallic Corrosion," Trans. Electrochem. Soc., 76, 161 (1939).

15. ROLE OF OXYGEN AND DEAERATION

a. H. O. Forrest, B. E. Roetheli, R. H. Brown and G. L. Cox, "The Initial Corrosion Rate of Steel," etc., Ind. Eng. Chem., 22, 1197 (1930); 23, 350, 650, 1010, 1012 (1931).

b. K. A. Kobe and W. L. Gooding, "Oxygen Removal from Boiler Feed Water by Sodium Sulfite," J. Ind. Eng. Chem., 27, 331-333 (1935).

c. R. B. Mears and U. R. Evans, "The Probability of Corrosion," Trans. Faraday Soc., 31, 527 (1935).

d. R. M. Hitchens and R. W. Towne, Proc. A. S. T. M., 36, Part II, 687 (1936).

e. S. T. Powell and H. S. Burns, "Vacuum Deaeration Combats Cold Water Corrosion," Chem. and Met. Eng., 43, 180 (1936).

f. R. E. Hall, "A New Approach to the Problems of Conditioning Water for Steam Generators," Trans. A.S.M.E., 66, 457 (1944).

g. W. E. Pratt, "Effects of Oxygen Exhaustion from Corrosive Solutions on High Nickel-Chromium-Molybdenum Alloy Steels," Trans. Electrochem. Soc., 86, 203 (1944).

h. M. G. Fontana and F. H. Beck, "Nature and Mechanism of Passivity of 18-8 Stainless Steel," Metal Progress, 51, 939 (1947).

i. R. C. Alexander and J. K. Rummel, "Feedwater Treatment During Early Operation of Steam-Electric Stations," Trans. A.S.M.E., 72, 529-532 (1950).

j. W. I. Whitton, "The Corrosion of Iron Covered by a Thin Film of Neutral Salt Solution," Trans. Faraday Soc., 46, Part II, pp. 927-938 (1950).

k. W. A. Patrick and H. B. Wagner, "Mechanism of Oxygen Reduction at an Iron Cathode," Corrosion, 6, 34-38 (1950).

l. M. J. Pryor and M. Cohen, "Role of Dissolved Oxygen During the Inhibition of the Corrosion of Iron by Sodium Phosphate Solution," Nature, 167, No. 4239, 157 (1951) Jan. 27.

m. R. V. Comeaux, "Role of Oxygen in Corrosion and Cathodic Protection," Corrosion, 8, 305 (1952).

16. CATHODIC PROTECTION

a. R. H. Brown and R. B. Mears, "Cathodic Protection," Trans. Electrochem. Soc., 81, 455 (1942).

b. E. G. Carlson, "Use of Forced Drainage Systems in Stray Current Areas," Corrosion, 1, 31 (1945).

c. "Cathodic Protection—A Symposium"—Pittsburgh, Pa. 1947—Published 1949, National Association of Corrosion Engineers, Houston, Texas.

d. Sir H. Davy—See reference No. 10.

e. I. A. Denison and M. Romanoff, "Behavior of Experimental Zinc-Steel Couples Underground," J. Res. Nat. Bu. Stds., 40, #4, pp. 301-313 (RP1876) (1948).

f. H. A. Humble, "The Cathodic Protection of Steel in Sea Water with Magnesium Anodes," Corrosion, 4, 358-370 (1948).

g. G. L. Doremus and M. E. Parker, Jr., "Engineering Aspects of Cathodic Protection as Applied to Pipe Lines," Corrosion, 5, 273 (1949).

h. H. A. Humble, "The Cathodic Protection of Steel Piling in Sea Water," Corrosion, 5, 292-302 (1949).

i. G. R. Olson and H. V. Beasley, "Practical Corrosion Control on Gas Transmission Lines," Corrosion, 5, 249 (1949).

j. F. J. LeFebvre and L. P. Sudrabin, "Some Observations of the Effect of Cathodic Protection on Rust Tubercle pH," J. New England Water Works Assoc., 64, 309 (1950).

k. H. D. Holler, "Studies on Galvanic Couples, III, Polarization and Cathodic Protection," J. Electrochem. Soc., 97, 453-461 (1950).

l. S. Schuldiner, "The Cathodic Protection of Ships' Hulls in Sea Water—A Critical Review," U. S. Naval Research Laboratory (PB101169), 65 pp., Jan. (1950).

m. C. R. Draughan, Jr. and E. B. McNeil, "Cathodic Protection for Open-Box Type Coolers," Oil and Gas J., 49, No. 4, 76-78, (1950), June 1; Petroleum Refiner, 29, No. 5, 97-103 (1950) May.

n. K. N. Barnard and G. L. Christie, "Cathodic Protection of an Active Ship in Sea Water," Corrosion, 6, 232 (1950); 7, 114 (1951).

o. F. L. LaQue, "Protection of Steel in Off-Shore Structures," Drilling, 11, No. 8, 29-31, 102-103 (1950).

p. K. N. Barnard, "Use of Magnesium Alloy Anodes on Ship Bottoms," Can. J. Res., 28, Sect. F, #11, pp. 417-437 (1950).

q. S. P. Ewing, "Potential Measurements for Determining Cathodic Protection Requirements," Corrosion, 7, 410 (1951).

r. W. A. Deringer and F. W. Nelson, "A Field Investigation of Cathodic Protection in Glass Lined and Galvanized Water Heaters," Corrosion, 8, 57 (1952).

s. O. Osborn and H. A. Robinson, "Performance of Magnesium Galvanic Anodes in Underground Service," Corrosion, 8, 114 (1952).

t. W. J. Schwerdtfeger and O. N. McDorman, "Potential and Current Requirements for the Cathodic Protection of Steel in Soil," Corrosion, 8, 391-398 (1952).

17. PASSIVITY

a. H. H. Uhlig and J. Wulff, "The Nature of Passivity in Stainless Steels and Other Alloys," Trans. Am. Inst. Min. Met. Engrs., 135, 494 (1936); ibid., 140, 387 (1940).

b. H. H. Uhlig, "Passivity in Copper-Nickel and Molybdenum - Nickel - Iron Alloys," Trans. Electrochem. Soc., 85, 207-218 (1944).

c. M. G. Fontana and F. H. Beck, "Nature and Mechanism of Passivity of 18-8 Stainless Steel," Metal Progress, 51, 939 (1947).

d. L. Guitton, "The Passivity of Stainless Steels and the Phenomena of Adsorption," Compt. rend., 226, 805-807 (1948).

e. R. Piontelli, "Consideration of the Passivity of metals," Metaux et Corrosion, 23, 1948, (273), 124-135.

f. H. H. Uhlig, "Passivity in Chromium-Iron Alloys: Adsorbed Films on Chromium," Trans. A.I.M.M.E., 175, 710 (1948).

g. U. R. Evans, "Some European Researches on Passivity," Corrosion, 4, 545-556 (1948).

h. R. B. Mears, "A Unified Mechanism of Passivity and Inhibition," Trans. Electrochem. Soc., 95, 1-10 (1949).

i. M. Pourbaix, "Corrosion, Passivity and Passivation from the Thermodynamic Point of View," Corrosion, 5, 121-133 (1949).

j. J. M. Defranoux, "Passivation of Stainless Steels in Certain Strong Acids," Compt. rend., 231, 901 (1950).

k. R. Speiser, F. H. Beck, M. G. Fontana and E. N. Lassettre, "Passivation of Metals," J. Chem. Phys., 18, 772 (1950).

l. U. R. Evans and I. D. G. Berwick, "The Passivity of Metals—Part XI—The Anodic Behavior of Iron Oxide Films," J. Chem. Soc., 1952, pp. 3432-3437, and earlier papers by U. R. Evans and co-workers in the same journal beginning with "The Passivity of Metals—Part I—The Isolation of the Protective Film," J. Chem. Soc., May, 1927.

18. ALLOYING OR ADJUSTMENT OF COMPOSITION

a. D. M. Buck, "Copper in Steel, Influence on Corrosion," J. Ind. Eng. Chem., 5, 447 (1913).

b. E. Houdremont and P. Schafmeister, "Prevention of Intergranular Corrosion in 18% Chromium-8% Nickel Steel," Arch. Eisenhuttenw., 7, 187 (1933).

c. W. Lynes, "Comparative Value of Arsenic, Antimony and Phosphorus in Preventing Dezincification," Proc. A.S.T.M., 41, 859 (1941).

d. F. L. LaQue, "The Behavior of Nickel-Copper Alloys in Sea Water," J. Soc. Nav. Engrs., 53, Feb. (1941), #1, p. 29.

e. H. J. French and F. L. LaQue, "Alloy Constructional Steels," American Society for Metals, Cleveland, Ohio (1942).

f. J. D. Hanawalt, C. E. Nelson and J. A. Peloubet, "Corrosion Studies of Magnesium and Its Alloys," Trans. A.I.M.M.E., Inst. Met. Div., 147, 273 (1942).

g. F. M. Becket and R. Franks, "Effects of Columbium in Chromium-Nickel Steels," Trans. A.I.M.M.E., 113, 143 (1943).

h. H. R. Copson, "A Theory on the Mechanism of Rusting of Low Alloy Steels in the Atmosphere," Proc. A.S.T.M., 45, 554 (1945).

i. A. W. Tracy and R. L. Hungerford, "The Effect of the Iron Content of Cupro-Nickel on its Corrosion Resistance in 'Sea Water,'" Proc. A.S.T.M., 45, 591 (1945).

j. C. P. Larrabee, "Effect of Composition and Environment on Corrosion of Iron and Steel," Symposium on Corrosion of Metals, Amer. Soc. Metals (1946).

k. G. C. Kiefer and C. M. Sheriden, "Effect of Composition on Low Carbon Austenitic Chromium-Nickel Stainless Steels," Yearbook Am. Iron Steel Inst. (1948).

l. W. O. Binder, C. R. Brown and R. Franks, "Resistance to Sensitization of Austenitic Chromium-Nickel Steels of 0.03 Percent Maximum Carbon Content," Am. Soc. Metals, Preprint No. 25 (1950).

m. B. J. Kelly, "Corrosion of Railroad Hopper Car Body Sheets," Corrosion, 7, 196-201 (1951).

n. W. C. Stewart and F. L. LaQue, "Corrosion Resisting Characteristics of Iron Modified 90-10 Cupro-Nickel Alloy," Corrosion, 8, 259-277 (1952).

19. INHIBITORS

a. H. P. Munger, "Use of Inhibitors in Pickling Iron," Trans. Electrochem. Soc., 69, 85 (1936).

b. A. A. Berk, "Observations on the Use of Cyclohexylamine in Steam-Heating Systems," Bureau of Mines, R. I. 3754, June, (1944).

c. C. F. Bonilla, "Pipe Service Tests in Baltimore Water," Trans. Electrochem. Soc., 87, 237 (1945).

d. M. Darrin, "Chromate Corrosion Inhibitors in Bimetallic Systems," J. Ind. Eng. Chem., 37, 741 (1945).

e. G. B. Hatch and O. Rice, "Corrosion Control with Threshold Treatment," J. Ind. Eng. Chem., 37, 752 (1945).

f. W. Stericker, "Protection of Small Water Systems from Corrosion," J. Ind. Eng. Chem., 37, 716 (1945).

g. D. H. Green and R. A. Willihnganz, "Problems of Automotive Cooling System Corrosion Inhibition," Steel, 119, Oct. 14 (1946), p. 168.

h. H. H. Uhlig, "The Mechanism of the Action of Corrosion Inhibitors," Metaux et Corrosion, 22, 204-10 (1947).

i. L. Cavallero, "Contribution to the Study of the Measurement and Mechanism of Action of Corrosion Inhibitors," Metaux et Corrosion, 23, 1948, #275/276, pp. 184-190.

j. S. T. Powell, H. E. Bacon and E. L. Knoedler, "Corrosion Prevention by Controlled Calcium Carbonate Scale," J. Ind. Eng. Chem., 40, 453 (1948).

k. N. Hackerman, "Use of Inhibitors in Corrosion Control," Corrosion, 4, 45-60 (1948).

l. D. A. Shock, "Testing and Selection of Inhibitors for Corrosive High Pressure Condensate Wells," Corrosion, 4, 179-185 (1948).

m. M. Darrin, "Corrosion Inhibitors in Recirculating Water Systems," Can. Chem. Process Ind., 33, 512 (1949).

n. M. L. Davis, "Use of Corrosion Inhibitors in De-Icing Salts," Proc. Public Works Congr., 55, 236 (1949).

o. M. Pourbaix and P. van Rysselberghe, "An Electrochemical Mechanism of Corrosion Inhibitors by Chromates, Nitrites and Other Oxidants," Corrosion, 6, 313-315 (1950).

p. C. M. Blair, "Some Applications of Organic Corrosion Inhibitors in the Petroleum Industry," Corrosion, 7, 189 (1951).

q. A. Wachter, T. Skei and N. Skillman, "Dicyclohexyl Ammonium Nitrate, A Volatile Inhibitor for Corrosion Preventive Packaging," Corrosion, 7, 284 (1951).

r. H. R. Baker and W. A. Zisman, "Liquid and Vapor Corrosion Inhibitors," Lubrication Eng., 7, 117 (1951).

20. HUMIDITY CONTROL

  a. R. L. Hockley, "New Dehydration Packaging Method," Chem. Eng. News, 21, 2132 (1943).

  b. G. C. Wells, "The Importance of Controlled Humidity in Long Time Preservation," Corrosion and Materials Protection, 5, No. 5, (Sept.-Oct.) 1948, p. 4.

  c. O. V. Zarubina, "Temperature and Humidity Factors in the Corrosion of Metals in a Sulfur Dioxide Atmosphere," Zhur. Prik. Khim., 21, 362-371 (1948).

  d. F. Ogburn, E. R. Weaver and W. Blum, "Effects of Relative Humidity and Surface Condition Upon the Corrosion of Low Carbon Steel and Zinc," Metaux et Corrosion, 25, #283, (1949), pp. 77-84.

  e. G. Jaubert, "The Protection of Aero Engines Against Rust and the Deceptive Indication Given by Cobalt Chloride As a Hygrometric Indicator," Compt. rend., 228, pp. 826-828 (1949).

21. PROTECTIVE COATINGS (Organic)

  a. H. R. Clauser, "Protecting Surface Finish with Shippable Plastic Coatings," Materials and Methods, 26, July 1947, #1, pp. 70-74.

  b. H. Seller, "Rust Preventives — How They Work, What They Contain," Chem. Ind., 62, #1, pp. 62-64 (1948).

  c. R. McFarland, "Combatting Corrosion with Rubber Linings," Corrosion, 5, 98-99 (1949).

  d. H. A. Pray and R. S. Peoples, "Paints for Enclosed Structural Members in Steel Housing Construction," Steel, 125, Oct. 20, 1949, #16, 63-70.

  e. H. Wagner, "Mechanism of Pigmentation of Anti-Corrosive Paints and Varnishes," Corrosion, 6, 22 (1950).

  f. S. L. Miller, "Field Experience with Corrosion Protection of Galvanized Steel Substation Structures," Corrosion, 6, 120-122 (1950).

  g. J. C. Hudson, "Performance of Anti-Corrosive Compositions in Sea Water—Effect of Surface Preparation of Steel," J. Iron Steel Inst., 165, July, 1950, 3, pp. 314-334.

  h. J. T. Crennell, "Electrochemical Behavior of Paint Films in Sea Water," J. Soc. Chem. Ind., 69, #12, pp. 371-3 (1950).

  i. W. W. Cranmer, "Gasoline Resistant Tank Coatings," Corrosion, 8, 195-204 (1952).

22. C. H. Sample, "Choice of Electrodeposited Coatings," Plating, 37, #5, 482-484; #6, 618, 623-624 (1950).

23. DESIGN

  a. F. L. LaQue and G. L. Cox, "Some Observations on the Potentials of Metals," Proc. Amer. Soc. Testing Mat., 40, 670 (1940).

  b. P. Ffield, "Recommendations for Using Steel Piping in Salt Water Systems," J. Amer. Soc. Naval Engrs., 57, Feb. 1945, pp. 1-20.

  c. G. W. Seagren and F. L. LaQue, "The Effectiveness of Paint in Suppressing Galvanic Corrosion," Corrosion, 2, 67 (1946).

  d. R. B. Mears and R. H. Brown, "Designing to Prevent Corrosion," Corrosion, 3, 97 (1947).